Mike Fink, King of the Keel-Boatmen

Their Weight in Wildcats. *Tales of* *The Frontier*

ILLUSTRATED BY JAMES DAUGHERTY

HOUGHTON MIFFLIN COMPANY·BOSTON

The Riverside Press Cambridge

1936

'... Stripedest, kickingest kittens escaped,
Caterwauling "Yankee Doodle Dandy,"
Renounced their poor relations,
Crossed the Appalachians,
And turned to tiny tigers
In the humorous forest ...

'... The smallest, blindest puppies toddled west
While their eyes were coming open,
And, with misty observations,
Crossed the Appalachians,
Barked, barked, barked
At the glow-worms and the marsh lights and the
        lightning-bugs
And turned to ravening wolves
Of the forest ...'[1]

[1] From *In Praise of Johnny Appleseed* by Vachel Lindsay. Reprinted
with the permission of the publisher, The Macmillan Company.

Editorial Note

'Well, I will walk tall into varmint and Indian; it's a way I've got, and it comes as natural as grinning to a hyena. I'm a regular tornado — tough as a hickory — and long-winded as a nor'-wester. I can strike a blow like a falling tree — and every lick makes a gap in the crowd that lets in an acre of sunshine. Whew, boys!...'

MIKE FINK, King of the Keel-Boatmen, is on deck. Though he would have pitched overboard the first man to suggest it, he might have been speaking for almost any of the frontier heroes who appear in this book. They could, as the saying goes, whip their weight in wildcats. The tall tales which they told about themselves, or which rumor has gathered about them, include some of the grandest reading in American literature. While some were more modest or less articulate than others, they generally managed to give rumor a flying start.

This book is made up of characteristic yarns of these pioneer giants — Indian fighters, trappers, hunters, fur-traders, boatmen, lumberjacks — interpreted in line and color by Mr. James Daugherty. Needless to say, one small volume can at best ladle out only a taste here and there from a very potent brew. The object has been to bring together an artist and a subject perfectly

in tune with each other and to offer a sample of a literature that deserves to be better known.

Several of these selections are from autobiographies;
the remainder, with a few exceptions, are also from
original sources or from early accounts which preserve
the flavor of the period with which they deal. The
stories range in character from the supposedly factual
to the purely humorous and wildly imaginative; in
geography, they extend from Ohio to Texas, from Virginia to the Far Northwest; in time, from Revolution-
ary days to the living present — for the Negroes still
sing of John Henry, and the lumberjacks add yearly
to the fabulous feats of Paul Bunyan and Babe the
Blue Ox. Though they may be as different from one
another as was rough Mike Fink from gentle Johnny
Appleseed, these tales have something very important
in common — something which finds graphic expression
in Mr. Daugherty's muscular drawings. It is the joy-
ful strength and shameless extravagance of America
in her Heroic Age.

Contents

Illustrations

Introduction

IN FASHIONING these sketches little or nothing has been added historically and factually to that gorgeous visual record that Remington, Bodmer, and Catlin have made of the Old West as it came red and roaring in all its actual splendor to their keen eyes and hands. But out of the underlying tempo and rhythm of these stories I have tried to sense and to make some image or pattern that might suggest the sprawling fecundity, the shiftless ingenuity, the vast human drama of the old frontier. I have tried to call up the robust images, the wild processionals, the swift, fierce action and encounters — and all this feebly with a tiny brush, a scrap of paper, a pot of ink, and a large enthusiasm.

The immense lore behind these few tales and sketches is, it seems to me, a vast Iliad and Odyssey in the raw, from which writers and painters and sculptors will be taking themes and building up glorious songs and dramas and colossal carved and painted friezes and façades and processionals as long as the genial, tough, cantankerous spirit of America endures.

JAMES DAUGHERTY

Kentucky

Mike Fink, The Keel-Boatman

The Disgraced Scalp-lock

By T. B. Thorpe. From 'The
Hive of the Bee-Hunter,' 1854

IN ALL the howling wilderness of young America, there were no harder, tougher, 'ring-tailed roarers' than the boatmen of the Ohio and the Mississippi. Mike Fink was their leader, by right of conquest. He could shoot straighter, fight harder, drink deeper, boast louder, than any 'critter, human or inhuman,' west of the Alleghenies. He was born at Fort Pitt in 1770, probably of Scotch-Irish parents; he died about 1823. At the age of seventeen he had already become famous for his uncanny skill with a rifle. For several years thereafter he served as an Indian scout. Then he passed the supreme test — he whipped a keel-boatman and won himself a berth on the river.

'With the freer ways of the water,' writes Constance Rourke, 'the boatman perhaps emerged more quickly as master of his scene than did the backwoodsman.' These were the hardy forerunners of the pilots classically portrayed by Mark Twain in *Life on the Mississippi*. They learned to know every snag, sand bar, rock, and eddy in the ever-changing river. They were equally prepared to repel an Indian raid at midnight, break up a camp meeting ashore, fight all comers rough-an'-tumble, or 'shoot the cup' on each other's heads, with drunken oaths of undying friendship. They developed huge muscles in poling the long narrow keelboats upstream against the current. (Mike Fink was primarily a keel-boatman, though occasionally he worked on one of the wide flatboats, or 'broadhorns,' such as appears in the following story.) They were the gamecocks of the wilderness.

During Mike's lifetime, stories of his prowess and his rough practical jokes circulated from Pittsburgh to the Gulf. The first literary treatment of his exploits, however, did not appear until 1829, six years after his death. One of the best Fink tales, 'The Disgraced Scalp-lock, or Incidents on Western Waters,' written by T. B. Thorpe, appeared in *The Spirit of the Times* in 1842, being reprinted in Thorpe's *The Hive of the Bee-Hunter* (Appleton, 1854), under the title, 'Mike Fink, the Keel-Boatman.' A full account of the hero's life, with an extensive bibliography, will be found in *Mike Fink*, by Walter Blair and Franklin J. Meine (Holt, 1933).

Mike Fink
The Keel-Boatman

OCCASIONALLY may be seen on the Ohio and Mississippi rivers singularly hearty-looking men, who would puzzle a stranger as to their history and age. Their bodies always exhibit a powerful development of muscle and bone; their cheeks are prominent, and you would pronounce them men enjoying perfect health in middle life, were it not for their heads, which, if not entirely bald, will be but sparsely covered with steel-gray hair.

Another peculiarity about this people is that they have a singular knowledge of all the places on the river; every bar and bend is spoken of with precision and familiarity; every town is recollected before it was half as large as the present, or 'when it was no town at all.' Innumerable places are marked out by them where once was an Indian fight or a rendezvous of robbers.

Among the flatboatmen there were none who gained more notoriety than Mike Fink. His name is still remembered along the whole of the Ohio, as a man who excelled his fellows in everything — particularly in his rifle-shot, which was acknowledged to be unsurpassed. Probably no man ever lived who could compete with Mike in the latter accomplishment. Strong as Hercules, free from all nervous excitement, possessed of perfect health, and familiar with his weapon from childhood, he raised the rifle to his eye, and, having once taken sight, it was as firmly fixed as if buried in a rock.

The rifle was Mike's pride, and he rejoiced on all occasions where he could bring it into use, whether it was turned against the beast of prey or the more savage Indian: and in his day, the last named was the common foe with whom Mike and his associates had to contend.

On the occasion when we would particularly introduce Mike to the reader, he had bound himself for a while to the pursuits of trade, until a voyage from the headwaters of the Ohio and down the Mississippi could be completed. Heretofore he had kept himself exclusively to the Ohio, but a liberal reward, and some curiosity, prompted him to extend his business character beyond his ordinary habits and inclinations.

In the accomplishment of this object, he lolled carelessly over the big 'sweep' that guided the 'flat' on which he officiated; the current of the river bore the boat swiftly along, and made his labor light. Wild and uncultivated as Mike appeared, he loved nature, and had a soul that sometimes felt, while admiring it, an exalted enthusiasm.

The beautiful Ohio was his favorite stream. From where it runs no stronger than a gentle rivulet to where it mixes with the muddy Mississippi, Mike was as familiar with its meanderings as a child could be with those of a flower-garden. He could not help noticing with sorrow the desecrating hand of improvement as he passed along, and half soliloquizing, and half addressing his companions, he broke forth:

'I knew these parts afore a squatter's axe had blazed a

tree; 'twasn't then pulling a —— sweep to get a living, but pulling the trigger, did the business. Those were times to see — a man might call himself lucky then.

'What's the use of improvements?

'When did cutting down trees make deer more plenty?

'Who ever found wild buffalo, or a brave Indian, in a city? Where's the fun, the frolicking, the fighting? Gone! Gone!

'The rifle won't make a man a living now — he must turn mule and work. If forests continue this way to be used up, I may yet be smothered in a settlement. Boys, this 'ere life won't do. I'll stick to the broadhorn 'cordin' to contract; but once done with it, I'm off for a frolic. If the Choctaws or Cherokees on the Mississippi don't give us a brush as we pass along, I shall grow as poor as a starved wolf in a pitfall.

'I must, to live peaceably, point my rifle at something more dangerous than varmint. Six months and no fight would spile me worse than a 'tack of rheumatism.'

Mike ceased speaking. The then beautiful village of Louisville appeared in sight; the labor of landing the boat occupied his attention — the bustle and confusion that followed such an incident ensued; and Mike was his own master by law, until his employers ceased trafficking and again required his services.

At the time we write of, a great many renegade Indians lived about the settlements, which is still the case in the extreme southwest. These Indians are generally the most degraded of their tribe — outcasts who, for crime or dissipation, are no longer allowed to associate with their people; they live by hunting or stealing, and spend, in the towns, their precarious gains in intoxication.

Among the throng that crowded on the flatboat on his arrival were a number of these unfortunate beings; they were influenced by no other motive than that of loitering round in idle speculation at what was going on.

Mike was attracted toward them at sight; and as he was idle, and consequently in the situation that is deemed most favorable to mischief, it struck him that it was a good opportunity to have a little sport at the Indians' expense.

Without ceremony, he gave a terrific war-whoop; and then, mixing the language of the aborigines and his own together, he went on savage fashion, and bragged of his triumphs and victories on the warpath, with all the seeming earnestness of a real 'brave.' Nor were taunting words spared to exasperate the poor creatures, who, while perfectly helpless, listened to the tales of their own greatness, and their own shame, until wound up to the highest pitch of impotent exasperation. Mike's companions joined in; thoughtless boys caught the spirit of the affair; and the Indians were goaded until they, in turn, made battle with their tongues.

Then commenced a system of running against them, pulling off their blankets, joined with a thousand other indignities; finally the Indians made a precipitate retreat ashore, amid the hooting and jeering of a thoughtless crowd which considered them as poor devils, destitute of both feeling and humanity.

Among this band of outcasts was a Cherokee who bore the name of Proud Joe; what his real cognomen was no one knew, for he was taciturn, haughty — and, in spite of his poverty and his manner of life, won the name we have mentioned. His face was expressive of talent, but it was furrowed by the most terrible habits of drunkenness.

That he was a superior Indian was admitted; and it was also understood that he was banished from his mountain home, his tribe being then numerous and powerful, for some great crime. He was always looked up to by his companions, and managed, however intoxicated he might be, to sustain a singularly proud bearing, which did not even depart from him while prostrate on the ground.

Joe was careless of his person and habits — in this respect he was behind his fellows; but one ornament of his was attended to with a care which would have done honor to him if still surrounded by his people, and amid his native woods. Joe still wore, with Indian dignity, his scalp-lock; he ornamented it with taste, and cherished it, as report said, until some Indian messenger of vengeance should tear it from his head, as expiatory of his numerous crimes. Mike had noticed this peculiarity; and, reaching out his hand, plucked from the revered scalplock a hawk's feather.

The Indian glared horribly on Mike as he consummated the insult, snatched the feather from his hand, then shaking his clenched fist in the air, as if calling on Heaven for revenge, retreated with his friends.

Mike saw that he had roused the soul of the savage, and he marveled wonderfully that so much resentment should be exhibited; and as an earnest to Proud Joe that the wrong he had done him should not rest unrevenged, he swore that he would cut the scalp-lock off close to his head, the first convenient opportunity, and then he thought no more about it.

The morning following the arrival of the boat at Louisville was occupied in making preparations to pursue the voyage down the river. Nearly everything was completed, and Mike had taken his favorite place at the sweep, when, looking up the river-bank, he beheld at some distance Joe and his companions, and perceived, from their gesticulations, that they were making him the subject of conversation.

Mike thought instantly of several ways in which he could show them, altogether, a fair fight, and then whip them with ease; he also reflected with what extreme satisfaction he would enter into the spirit of the arrangement, and other matters to him equally pleasing — when all the Indians disappeared, save Joe himself, who stood at times viewing Mike in moody silence, and then staring round at passing objects.

From the peculiarity of Joe's position to Mike, who was below him, his head and the upper part of his body were relieved boldly against the sky, and in one of his movements he brought his profile face to view. The prominent scalp-lock and its adornments seemed to be more striking

than ever, and again roused the pugnacity of Mike Fink;
in an instant he raised his rifle, always loaded and at com-
mand, brought it to his eye, and, before he could be prevented, drew sight upon Proud Joe, and fired. The ball
whistled loud and shrill, and Joe, springing his whole
length into the air, fell upon the ground.

The cold-blooded murder was noticed by fifty persons
at least, and there arose from the crowd a universal cry of
horror and indignation at the bloody deed. Mike himself
seemed to be much astonished, and in an instant reloaded
his rifle, and, as a number of white persons rushed toward
the boat, Mike threw aside his coat, and, taking his
powderhorn between his teeth, leaped, rifle in hand, into
the Ohio, and commenced swimming for the opposite
shore.

Some bold spirits determined that Mike should not so
easily escape, and, jumping into the only skiff at com-
mand, pulled swiftly after him. Mike watched their
movements until they came within a hundred yards of
him, then turning in the water, he supported himself by
his feet alone, and raised his deadly rifle to his eye. Its
muzzle, if it spoke hostilely, was as certain to send a messenger of death through one or more of his pursuers as if it
were lightning, and they knew it; they dropped their oars,
and silently returned to the shore. Mike waved his hand
towards the little village of Louisville, and again pursued
his way.

The time consumed by the firing of Mike's rifle, the
pursuit, and the abandonment of it required less time than
we have taken to give the detail; and in that time, to the
astonishment of the gaping crowd around Joe, they saw
him rising with a bewildered air; a moment more — he

recovered his senses and stood up — at his feet lay his scalp-lock!

The ball had cut it clear from his head; the cord around the root, in which were placed feathers and other ornaments, still held it together, the concussion had merely stunned its owner; further — he had escaped all bodily harm! A cry of exultation rose at the last evidence of the skill of Mike Fink — the exhibition of a shot that established his claim, indisputably, to the eminence he ever afterward held — that of the unrivaled marksman of all the flatboatmen of the Western waters.

Proud Joe had received many insults. He looked upon himself as a degraded, worthless being — and the ignominy heaped upon him he never, except by reply, resented; but this last insult was like seizing the lion by the mane, or a Roman senator by the beard — it roused the slumbering demon within, and made him again thirst to resent his wrongs, with an intensity of emotion that can only be felt by an Indian. His eye glared upon the jeering crowd like a fiend; his chest swelled and heaved until it seemed that he must suffocate.

No one noticed this emotion. All were intent upon the exploit that had so singularly deprived Joe of his warlock; and, smothering his wrath, he retreated to his associates with a consuming fire at his vitals. He was a different being from what he had been an hour before; and with that desperate resolution on which a man stakes his all, he swore, by the Great Spirit of his forefathers, that he would be revenged.

An hour after the disappearance of Joe, both he and Mike Fink were forgotten. The flatboat, which the latter had deserted, was got under way, and, dashing through the rapids in the river opposite Louisville, wended on its course. As is customary when night sets in, the boat was securely fastened in some little bend or bay in the shore, where it remained until early morn.

Long before the sun had fairly risen, the boat was again pushed into the stream, and it passed through a valley presenting the greatest possible beauty and freshness of landscape that the mind can conceive.

It was spring, and a thousand tints of green developed themselves in the half-formed foliage and bursting buds. The beautiful mallard skimmed across the water, ignorant of the danger of the white man's approach; the splendid spoonbill decked the shallow places near the shore, while myriads of singing birds filled the air with their unwritten songs.

In the far reaches down the river, there occasionally might be seen a bear stepping along the ground as if dainty of its feet; and, snuffing the intruder on his wild home, he would retreat into the woods.

To enliven all this, and give the picture the look of humanity, there was also seen, struggling with the floating mists, a column of blue smoke, which came from a fire built on a projecting point of land, around which the current swept rapidly, hurrying past everything that floated on the river. The eye of the boatmen saw the advantage which the situation of the place rendered to those on shore, to annoy and attack; and as wandering Indians, even in those days, did not hesitate to rob, there was much speculation as to what reception the boat would receive from the builders of the fire.

The rifles were all loaded, to be prepared for any kind of reception, and the loss of Mike Fink was lamented, as

A Flatboat on the Ohio

the prospect of a fight presented itself, where he could use with effect his terrible rifle. The boat in the meantime swept round the point; but instead of an enemy, there lay, in a profound sleep, Mike Fink, with his feet toasting at the fire; his pillow was a huge bear that had been shot on the day previous, while, scattered in profusion around him, were several deer and wild turkeys.

Mike had not been idle. After selecting a place most eligible for noticing the passing boat, he had spent his time in hunting — and was surrounded by trophies of his prowess. The scene that he presented was worthy of the time and the man, and would have thrown Landseer into a delirium of joy could he have witnessed it. The boat, owing to the swiftness of the current, passed Mike's resting-place, although it was pulled strongly to the shore. As Mike's companions came opposite to him, they raised a shout, half exultation at meeting him, and half to alarm him with the idea that Joe's friends were upon him. Mike, at the sound, sprang to his feet, rifle in hand, and as he looked around, he raised it to his eyes, and by the time that he discovered the boat, he was ready to fire.

'Down with your shooting-iron, you wild critter,' shouted one of the boatmen.

Mike dropped the piece, and gave a loud halloo, which echoed among the solitudes like a piece of artillery. The meeting between Mike and his fellows was characteristic. They joked and jibed him with their rough wit, and he parried it off with a most creditable ingenuity. Mike soon learned the extent of his rifle-shot — but he seemed perfectly indifferent to the fact that Proud Joe was not dead.

The only sentiment he uttered was regret that he did not fire at the vagabond's head, for if he hadn't hit it, why, he said that he would have made the first bad shot in twenty years. The dead game was carried on board the boat, the adventure was forgotten, and everything resumed the monotony of floating in a flatboat down the Ohio.

A month or more elapsed, and Mike had progressed several hundred miles down the Mississippi; his journey had been remarkably free from incident; morning, noon, and night presented the same banks, the same muddy water, and he sighed to see some broken land, some high hills, and he railed and swore that he should have been such a fool as to desert his favorite Ohio for a river that produced nothing but alligators; and was never, at best, half finished.

Occasionally, the plentifulness of game put him in spirits, but it did not last long; he wanted more lasting excitement, and declared himself as perfectly miserable and helpless as a wildcat without teeth or claws.

In the vicinity of Natchez rise a few abrupt hills, which tower above the surrounding lowlands of the Mississippi like monuments; they are not high, but from their loneliness and rarity they create sensations of pleasure and awe.

Under the shadow of one of these bluffs, Mike and his associates made the customary preparations for passing the night. Mike's enthusiasm knew no bounds at the sight of land again; he said it was as pleasant as 'close water to a fresh wound'; and, as his spirits rose, he went on making the region roundabout, according to his notions, an agreeable residence.

'The Choctaws live in these diggin's,' said Mike, 'and a cursed time they must have of it. Now if I lived in these parts I'd declare war on 'em just to have something to keep me from growing dull; without some such business I'd be as musty as an old swamp moccasin snake. I would build a cabin on that ar hill yonder, and could, from its location, with my rifle, repulse a whole tribe, if they dar'd to come after me.

'What a beautiful time I'd have of it! I never was particular about what's called a fair fight; I just ask half a chance, and the odds against me — and if I then don't keep clear of snags and sawyers, let me spring a leak and go to the bottom. It's natur that the big fish should eat the little ones. I've seen trout swallow a perch, and a cat would come along and swallow the trout, and perhaps, on the Mississippi, the alligators use up the cat, and so on to the end of the row.

'Well, I will walk tall into varmint and Indian; it's a way I've got, and it comes as natural as grinning to a hyena. I'm a regular tornado — tough as a hickory — and long-winded as a nor'wester. I can strike a blow like a falling tree — and every lick makes a gap in the crowd that lets in an acre of sunshine. Whew, boys!' shouted Mike, twirling his rifle like a walking-stick around his head, at the ideas suggested in his mind. 'Whew, boys! if the Choctaw divils in them ar woods thar would give us a brush, just as I feel now, I'd call them gentlemen. I must fight something, or I'll catch the dry rot — burnt brandy won't save me.'

As night wore on, one by one the hardy boatmen fell asleep, some in the confined interior, and others protected by a light covering in the open air.

The moon arose in beautiful majesty; her silver light, behind the highlands, gave them a power and theatrical effect as it ascended; and as its silver rays grew perpendicular, they kissed gently the summit of the hills, and poured down their full light upon the boat with almost noonday brilliancy.

But in the midst of the witchery of this quiet scene, there sounded forth the terrible rifle and the more terrible war-whoop of the Indian. One of the boatmen, asleep on deck, gave a stifled groan, turned upon his face, and with a quivering motion ceased to live.

Not so with his companions — they in an instant, as men accustomed to danger and sudden attacks, sprang ready-armed to their feet; but before they could discover their foes, seven sleek and horribly painted savages leaped from the hill into the boat. The firing of the rifle was useless, and each man singled out a foe and met him with the drawn knife.

The struggle was quick and fearful; and deadly blows were given, amid screams and imprecations that rent the air. Yet the voice of Mike Fink could be heard in encouraging shouts above the clamor.

'Give it to them, boys!' he cried. 'Cut their hearts out! Choke the dogs! Here's hell afire and the river rising!' Then, clenching with the most powerful of the assailants, he rolled with him upon the deck of the boat. Powerful as Mike was, the Indian seemed nearly a match for him. The two twisted and writhed like serpents — now one seeming to have the advantage and then the other.

In all this confusion there might occasionally be seen glancing in the moonlight the blade of a knife; but at whom the thrusts were made, or who wielded it, could not be discovered.

The general fight lasted less time then we have taken to describe it. The white men gained the advantage; two of the Indians lay dead upon the boat, and the living, escaping from their antagonists, leaped ashore, and before the rifle could be brought to bear they were out of its reach.

While Mike was yet struggling with his adversary, one of his companions cut the boat loose from the shore, and, with powerful exertion, managed to get its bows so far into the current that it swung round and floated; but before this was accomplished, and before anyone interfered with Mike, he was on his feet, covered with blood and blowing like a porpoise: by the time that he could get his breath, he commenced talking.

'Ain't been so busy in a long time,' said he, turning over his victim with his foot; 'that fellow fou't beautiful; if he's a specimen of the Choctaws that live in these parts, they are screamers. The infernal sarpents! The d——d 'possums!'

Talking in this way, he, with others, took a general

survey of the killed and wounded. Mike himself was a good deal cut up with the Indian's knife; but he called his wounds —— blackberry scratches. One of Mike's associates was severely hurt; the rest escaped comparatively harmless. The sacrifice was made at the first fire; for beside the dead Indians, there lay one of the boat's crew, cold and dead, his body perforated with four different balls. That he was the chief object of attack seemed evident, yet no one of his associates knew of his ever having had a single fight with the Indians.

The master of the broadhorn was a business man, and had often been down the Mississippi. This was the first attack he had received, or knew to have been made from the shores inhabited by the Choctaws, except by the white man; and he suggested the keeping the dead Indians until daylight, that they might have an opportunity to examine their dress and features, and see with certainty who were to blame for the occurrences of the night.

The dead boatman was removed with care to a respectful distance; and the living, except the person at the sweep of the boat, were soon buried in profound slumber.

Not until after the rude breakfast was partaken of, and the funeral rites of the dead boatman were solemnly performed, did Mike and his companions disturb the corpses of the red men.

Mike went about his business with alacrity. He stripped the bloody blanket from the Indian he had killed, as if it enveloped something requiring no respect. He examined carefully the moccasins on the Indian's feet, pronouncing them at one time Chickasaws — at another time, Shawnees. He stared at the livid face, but could not recognize the style of paint.

That the Indians were not strictly national in their adornments was certain, for they were examined by practiced eyes, that could have told the nation of the dead, if such had been the case, as readily as a sailor distinguishes a ship by its flag. Mike was evidently puzzled; and as he was about giving up his task as hopeless, the dead body he was examining was turned upon its side. Mike's eyes distended, as some of his companions observed, 'like a choked cat's,' and became riveted.

He drew himself up in a half-serious and half-comic expression, and pointing at the back of the dead Indian's head, there was exhibited a dead warrior in his paint, destitute of his scalp-lock — the small stump of which was only left being stiffened with red paint. Those who could read Indian symbols learned a volume of deadly resolve in what they saw. The body of Proud Joe was stiff and cold before them.

The last and best shot of Mike Fink had cost a brave man his life. The boatman so lately interred was evidently taken in the moonlight by Proud Joe and his party for Mike Fink, and they had risked their lives, one and all, that he might with certainty be sacrificed.

Nearly a thousand miles of swamp had been threaded, large and swift-running rivers had been crossed, hostile tribes passed through by Joe and his friends, that they might revenge the fearful insult of destroying, without the life, the sacred scalp-lock.

Johnny Appleseed

A Pioneer Hero

By W. D. Haley. From 'Harper's New Monthly,' 1871

JOHNNY APPLESEED, whose real name was John Chapman ('Jonathan' in the selection here) is one of the most lovable characters of the Frontier. He was the very antithesis of the rough hunter or Indian fighter. Impervious to frost and heat and snake-bite, possessed with marvelous powers of physical endurance, he was as gentle as he was tender-hearted. In his eyes it was a sin to inflict pain or death on man or beast. In place of a rifle he carried a volume of Swedenborg; scorning to boast of his own prowess, he devoted his energy to expounding the New Testament. His life's passion was the planting of apple trees and various useful herbs through the settlements in the wilderness. In the spirit of the true ascetic, he asked little material reward for his labors; when he did get paid for a bundle of apple saplings, it was generally in the form of old clothes or a supply of corn meal, or more likely still a promissory note which would never be collected. Once, under great provocation — when an itinerant preacher kept harking back to the bare feet and coarse raiment of the primitive Christians — he was heard quietly to exclaim: 'Here's your primitive Christian!'

John Chapman was born probably in Springfield or Boston, Massachusetts, about 1775; he died in Indiana in 1847. The main facts of his life, and the most interesting legends about him, are given in this selection from an article by W. D. Haley, in *Harper's New Monthly*, November, 1871.

Johnny Appleseed

THE first reliable trace of our modest hero finds him in the Territory of Ohio, in 1801, with a horse-load of apple seeds, which he planted in various places on and about the borders of Licking Creek, the first orchard thus originated by him being on the farm of Isaac Stadden, in what is now known as Licking County, in the State of Ohio. During the five succeeding years, although he was undoubtedly following the same strange occupation, we have no authentic account of his movements until we reach a pleasant spring day in 1806, when a pioneer settler in Jefferson County, Ohio, noticed a peculiar craft, with a remarkable occupant and a curious cargo, slowly dropping down with the current of the Ohio River. It was 'Johnny Appleseed,' by which name Jonathan Chapman was afterward known in every log-cabin from the Ohio River to the Northern lakes, and westward to the prairies of what is now the State of Indiana. With two canoes lashed together he was transporting a load of apple seeds to the Western frontier, for the purpose of creating orchards on the farthest verge of white settlements. With his canoes he passed down the Ohio to Marietta, where he entered the Muskingum, ascending the stream of that river until he reached the mouth of the

Walhonding, or White Woman Creek, and still onward, up the Mohican, into the Black Fork, to the head of navigation, in the region now known as Ashland and Richland Counties, on the line of the Pittsburgh and Fort Wayne Railroad, in Ohio. A long and toilsome voyage it was, as a glance at the map will show, and must have occupied a great deal of time, as the lonely traveler stopped at every inviting spot to plant the seeds and make his infant nurseries. These are the first well-authenticated facts in the history of Jonathan Chapman, whose birth, there is good reason for believing, occurred in Boston, Massachusetts, in 1775. According to this, which was his own statement in one of his less reticent moods, he was, at the time of his appearance on Licking Creek, twenty-six years of age, and whether impelled in his eccentricities by some absolute misery of the heart which could only find relief in incessant motion, or governed by a benevolent monomania, his whole after-life was devoted to the work of planting apple seeds in remote places. The seeds he gathered from the cider-presses of western Pennsylvania; but his canoe voyage in 1806 appears to have been the only occasion upon which he adopted that method of transporting them, as all his subsequent journeys were made on foot. Having planted his stock of seeds, he would return to Pennsylvania for a fresh supply, and, as sacks made of any less substantial fabric would not endure the hard usage of the long trip through forests dense with underbrush and briers, he provided himself with leathern bags. Securely packed, the seeds were conveyed, sometimes on the back of a horse, and not unfrequently on his own shoulders, either over a part of the old Indian trail that led from Fort Duquesne to Detroit, by way of Fort Sandusky, or over what is

Johnny Appleseed

styled in the appendix to Hutchins's 'History of Boguet's Expedition in 1764' the 'second route through the wilderness of Ohio,' which would require him to traverse a distance of one hundred and sixty-six miles in a west-northwest direction from Fort Duquesne in order to reach the Black Fork of the Mohican.

This region, although it is now densely populated, still possesses a romantic beauty that railroads and bustling towns cannot obliterate — a country of forest-clad hills and green valleys, through which numerous bright streams flow on their way to the Ohio; but when Johnny Appleseed reached some lonely log-cabin he would find himself in a veritable wilderness. The old settlers say that the margins of the streams, near which the first settlements were generally made, were thickly covered with a low, matted growth of small timber, which nearer to the water was a rank mass of long grass, interlaced with morning-glory and wild pea vines, among which funereal willows and clustering alders stood like sentinels on the outpost of civilization. The hills, that rise almost to the dignity of mountains, were crowned with forest trees, and in the coverts were innumerable bears, wolves, deer, and droves of wild hogs, that were as ferocious as any beast of prey. In the grass the massasauga and other venomous reptiles lurked in such numbers that a settler named Chandler has left the fact on record that during the first season of his residence, while mowing a little prairie which formed part of his land, he killed over two hundred black rattlesnakes in an area that would involve an average destruction of one of these reptiles for each rod of land. The frontiers-man, who felt himself sufficiently protected by his rifle against wild beasts and hostile Indians, found it necessary to guard against the attacks of the insidious enemies in the grass by wrapping bandages of dried grass around his buckskin leggings and moccasins; but Johnny would shoulder his bag of apple seeds, and with bare feet penetrate to some remote spot that combined picturesqueness and fertility of soil, and there he would plant his seeds, place a slight enclosure around the place, and leave them to grow until the trees were large enough to be transplanted by the settlers, who, in the meantime, would have made their clearings in the vicinity. The sites chosen by him are, many of them, well known, and are such as an artist or a poet would select — open places on the loamy lands that border the creeks, rich, secluded spots, hemmed in by giant trees, picturesque now, but fifty years ago, with their wild surroundings and the primal silence, they must have been tenfold more so.

In personal appearance Chapman was a small, wiry man, full of restless activity; he had long dark hair, a scanty beard that was never shaved, and keen black eyes that sparkled with a peculiar brightness. His dress was of the oddest description. Generally, even in the coldest weather, he went barefooted, but sometimes, for his long journeys, he would make himself a rude pair of sandals; at other times he would wear any cast-off foot-covering he chanced to find — a boot on one foot and an old brogan or a moccasin on the other. It appears to have been a matter of conscience with him never to purchase shoes, although he was rarely without money enough to do so. On one occasion, in an unusually cold November, while he was traveling barefooted through mud and snow, a settler who happened to possess a pair of shoes that were too small for his own use forced their acceptance upon Johnny, declaring that it was sinful for a human being to travel with naked feet in such weather. A few days afterward the donor was in the village that has since become the thriving city of Mansfield, and met his beneficiary contentedly plodding along with his feet bare and half frozen. With some degree of anger he inquired for the cause of such foolish conduct, and received for reply that Johnny had overtaken a poor, barefooted family moving Westward, and as they appeared to be in much greater need of clothing than he was, he had given them the shoes.

His dress was generally composed of cast-off clothing that he had taken in payment for apple-trees; and as the pioneers were far less extravagant than their descendants in such matters, the homespun and buckskin garments that they discarded would not be very elegant or serviceable. In his later years, however, he seems to have thought that even this kind of second-hand raiment was too luxurious, as his principal garment was made of a coffee sack, in which he cut holes for his head and arms to pass through, and pronounced it 'a very serviceable cloak, and as good clothing as any man need wear.' In the matter of headgear his taste was equally unique; his first experiment was with a tin vessel that served to cook his mush, but this was open to the objection that it did not protect his eyes from the beams of the sun; so he constructed a hat of pasteboard with an immense peak in front, and having thus secured an article that combined usefulness with economy, it became his permanent fashion.

Thus strangely clad, he was perpetually wandering through forests and morasses, and suddenly appearing in white settlements and Indian villages; but there must have been some rare force of gentle goodness dwelling in

his looks and breathing in his words, for it is the testimony of all who knew him that, notwithstanding his ridiculous attire, he was always treated with the greatest respect by the rudest frontiers-man, and, what is a better test, the boys of the settlements forbore to jeer at him. With grown-up people and boys he was usually reticent, but manifested great affection for little girls, always having pieces of ribbon and gay calico to give to his little favorites. Many a grandmother in Ohio and Indiana can remember the presents she received when a child from poor homeless Johnny Appleseed. When he consented to eat with any family he would never sit down to the table until he was assured that there was an ample supply for the children; and his sympathy for their youthful troubles and his kindness toward them made him friends among all the juveniles of the borders.

The Indians also treated Johnny with the greatest kindness. By these wild and sanguinary savages he was regarded as a 'great medicine man,' on account of his strange appearance, eccentric actions, and, especially, the fortitude with which he could endure pain, in proof of which he would often thrust pins and needles into his flesh. His nervous sensibilities really seem to have been less acute than those of ordinary people, for his method of treating the cuts and sores that were the consequences of his barefooted wanderings through briers and thorns was to sear the wound with a red-hot iron, and then cure the burn.

During the War of 1812, when the frontier settlers were tortured and slaughtered by the savage allies of Great Britain, Johnny Appleseed continued his wanderings, and was never harmed by the roving lands of hostile Indians. On many occasions the impunity with which he ranged the country enabled him to give the settlers warning of approaching danger in time to allow them to take refuge in their block-houses before the savages could attack them.

Our informant refers to one of these instances, when the news of Hull's surrender came like a thunder-bolt upon the frontier. Large bands of Indians and British were destroying everything before them and murdering defenseless women and children, and even the block-houses were not always a sufficient protection. At this time Johnny traveled day and night, warning the people of the approaching danger. He visited every cabin and delivered this message: 'The Spirit of the Lord is upon me, and He hath anointed me to blow the trumpet in the wilderness, and sound an alarm in the forest; for, behold, the tribes of the heathen are roundabout your doors, and a devouring flame followeth after them.' The aged man who narrated this incident said that he could feel even now the thrill that was caused by this prophetic announcement of the wild-looking herald of danger, who aroused the family on a bright moonlight midnight with his piercing voice. Refusing all offers of food and denying himself a moment's rest, he traversed the border day and night until he had warned every settler of the approaching peril.

In 1838 — thirty-seven years after his appearance on Licking Creek — Johnny noticed that civilization, wealth, and population were pressing into the wilderness of Ohio. Hitherto he had easily kept just in advance of the wave of settlement; but now towns and churches were making their appearance, and even, at long intervals, the stage-driver's horn broke the silence of the grand old forests, and he felt that his work was done in the region in which he had labored so long. He visited every house, and took a solemn farewell of all the families. The little girls who had been delighted with his gifts of fragments of calico and ribbons had become sober matrons, and the boys who had wondered at his ability to bear the pain caused by running needles into his flesh were heads of families. With parting words of admonition he left them, and turned his steps steadily toward the setting sun.

Colonel Boon

*By J. J. Audubon. From 'Or-
nithological Biography,' 1831*

B Y ACCUMULATION of myths and legends around a solid core of fact, Daniel Boone has evolved into a permanent symbol of the Frontier. He has overshadowed all his rivals, despite the fact that many of them are at least as deserving of lasting fame. Boone had the pioneer virtues of courage and strength and endurance; he had an unerring eye and a resourceful brain; he had — besides these commoner frontier gifts — a burning desire to settle 'the dark and bloody ground.' In contrast to Fink and the Mississippi 'screamers,' he is reputed to have been both modest and peace-loving — qualities which helped to make him a national idol.

Boone's life needs no retelling here. He was born near Reading, Pennsylvania, in 1734; he died in 1820, after penetrating all the way to Missouri, moved by the pioneer's eternal craving for elbow-room. Three years after his death, seven absurd stanzas in Byron's 'Don Juan' made him a world-wide celebrity. Two will be enough:

'Of all men, saving Sylla the manslayer,
    Who passes for, in life and death, most lucky,
Of the great names which in our faces stare,
    The Colonel Boon, backwoodsman of Kentucky,
Was happiest amongst mortals anywhere:
    For, killing nothing but a bear, or buck, he
Enjoyed the lonely, vigorous, harmless days
Of his old age, in wilds of deepest maze.

'Crime came not near him* — she is not the child
    Of solitude; health shrank not from him — for
Her home is in the rarely trodden wild,
    Where if men seek her not, and death be more
Their choice than life, forgive them as beguiled
    By habit to what their own hearts abhor —
In cities caged. The present case in point I
Cite is, that Boon lived hunting up to ninety.'

The following typical Boone story is to be found among the 'Delineations of American Scenery and Manners,' a series of valuable and delightful frontier sketches which Audubon included in his *Ornithological Biography*, published in 1831 to accompany the plates of *The Birds of America*.

* !

Colonel Boon

DANIEL BOON, or, as he was usually called in the Western Country, Colonel Boon, happened to spend a night with me under the same roof, more than twenty years ago. We had returned from a shooting excursion, in the course of which his extraordinary skill in the management of the rifle had been fully displayed. On retiring to the room appropriated to that remarkable individual and myself for the night, I felt anxious to know more of his exploits and adventures than I did, and accordingly took the liberty of proposing numerous questions to him.

The stature and general appearance of this wanderer of the Western forests approached the gigantic.[1] His chest was broad and prominent; his muscular powers displayed themselves in every limb; his countenance gave indication of his great courage, enterprise, and perseverance; and, when he spoke, the very motion of his lips brought the impression that whatever he uttered could not be otherwise than strictly true. I undressed, while he merely took off his hunting-shirt and arranged a few folds of blankets

[1] Commenting on this description, Constance Rourke writes: 'Boone was slender and under six feet, always appearing smaller than he was.' *American Humor*, p. 52.

on the floor, choosing rather to lie there, as he observed, than on the softest bed. When we had both disposed our- selves, each after his own fashion, he related to me the following account of his powers of memory, which I lay be- fore you, kind reader, in his own words, hoping that the simplicity of his style may prove interesting to you.

'I was once,' said he, 'on a hunting expedition on the banks of the Green River, when the lower parts of this State (Kentucky) were still in the hands of nature, and none but the sons of the soil were looked upon as its lawful proprietors. We Virginians had, for some time, been waging a war of intrusion upon them, and I, among the rest, rambled through the woods in pursuit of their race, as I now would follow the tracks of any ravenous animal. The Indians outwitted me one dark night, and I was as unexpectedly as suddenly made a prisoner by them.

'The trick had been managed with great skill; for no sooner had I extinguished the fire of my camp, and laid me down to rest in full security, as I thought, than I felt myself seized by an indistinguishable number of hands, and was immediately pinioned, as if about to be led to the scaffold for execution. To have attempted to be refrac- tory, would have proved useless and dangerous to my life, and I suffered myself to be removed from my camp to theirs, a few miles distant, without uttering even a word of complaint. You are aware, I dare say, that to act in this manner was the best policy, as you understand that, by so doing, I proved to the Indians at once that I was born and bred as fearless of death as any of themselves.

'When we reached the camp, great rejoicings were ex- hibited. Two squaws and a few papooses appeared par- ticularly delighted at the sight of me, and I was assured,

Daniel Boone

by every unequivocal gesture and word, that on the morrow the mortal enemy of the red-skins would cease to live. I never opened my lips, but was busy contriving some scheme which might enable me to give the rascals the slip before dawn. The women immediately fell a-searching about my hunting-shirt for whatever they might think valuable, and, fortunately for me, soon found my flask, filled with monongahela (that is, reader, strong whiskey). A terrific grin was exhibited on their murderous countenances, while my heart throbbed with joy at the anticipation of their intoxication. The crew immediately began to beat their bellies and sing, as they passed the bottle from mouth to mouth. How often did I wish the flask ten times its size, and filled with aqua fortis! I observed that the squaws drank more freely than the warriors, and again my spirits were about to be depressed, when the report of a gun was heard at a distance. The Indians all jumped on their feet. The singing and drinking were both brought to a stand, and I saw, with inexpressible joy, the men walk off to some distance and talk to the squaws. I knew that they were consulting about me, and I foresaw that, in a few moments, the warriors would go to discover the cause of the gun having been fired so near their camp. I expected that the squaws would be left to guard me. Well, sir, it was just so. They returned; the men took up their guns and walked away. The squaws sat down again, and, in less than five minutes, had my bottle up to their dirty mouths, gurgling down their throats the remains of the whiskey.

'With pleasure did I see them becoming more and more drunk, until the liquor took such hold of them that it was quite impossible for these women to be of any service.

They tumbled down, rolled about, and began to snore, when I, having no other chance of freeing myself from the cords that fastened me, rolled over and over towards the fire, and, after a short time, burned them asunder. I rose on my feet, stretched my stiffened sinews, snatched up my rifle, and for once in my life spared that of Indians. I now recollected how desirous I once or twice felt to lay open the skulls of the wretches with my tomahawk; but when I again thought upon killing beings unprepared, and unable to defend themselves, it looked like murder without need, and I gave up the idea.

'But, sir, I felt determined to mark the spot, and walking to a thrifty ash sapling, I cut out of it three large chips, and ran off. I soon reached the river, soon crossed it, and threw myself into the canebrakes, imitating the tracks of an Indian with my feet, so that no chance might be left for those from whom I had escaped to overtake me.

'It is now nearly twenty years since this happened, and more than five since I left the Whites' settlement, which I might never probably have visited again, had I not been called upon as a witness in a lawsuit which was pending in Kentucky, and which, I really believe, would never have been settled had I not come forward and established the beginning of a certain boundary line. The story is this, sir:

'Mr. —— moved from Old Virginia into Kentucky, and, having a large tract granted to him in the new State, laid claim to a certain parcel of land adjoining Green River, and, as chance would have it, took for one of his corners the very Ash tree on which I had made my mark, beginning, as it is expressed in the deed, "At an ash marked by three distinct notches of the tomahawk of a white man."

Boone Escapes from the Indians

'The tree had grown much, and the bark had covered the marks; but, somehow or other, Mr. —— had heard from someone all that I have already said to you, and, thinking that I might remember the spot alluded to in the deed, but which was no longer discoverable, wrote for me to come and try at least to find the place or the tree. His letter mentioned that all my expenses should be paid; and, not caring much about once more going back to Kentucky, I started and met Mr. ——. After some conversation, the affair with the Indians came to my recollection. I considered for a while, and began to think that, after all, I could find the very spot, as well as the tree, if it were yet standing.

'Mr. —— and I mounted our horses, and off we went to the Green River Bottoms. After some difficulty — for you must be aware, sir, that great changes have taken place in those woods — I found at last the spot where I had crossed the river, and, waiting for the moon to rise, made for the course in which I thought the ash tree grew. On approaching the place, I felt as if the Indians were still there, and as if I were still a prisoner among them. Mr. —— and I camped near what I conceived to be the spot, and waited until the return of day.

'At the rising of the sun I was on foot, and, after a good deal of musing, thought that an ash tree, then in sight, must be the very one on which I had made my mark. I felt as if there could be no doubt about it, and mentioned my thought to Mr. ——.

' "Well, Colonel Boon," said he, "if you think so I hope that it may prove true, but we must have some witnesses. Do you stay here about, and I will go and bring some of the settlers whom I know."

'I agreed. Mr. —— trotted off, and I, to pass the time, rambled about to see if a deer was still living in the land. But, ah! sir, what a wonderful difference thirty years makes in a country! Why, at the time when I was caught by the Indians, you would not have walked out in any direction more than a mile without shooting a buck or a bear. There were then thousands of buffaloes on the hills in Kentucky. The land looked as if it never would become poor; and to hunt in those days was a pleasure indeed. But when I was left to myself on the banks of Green River, I dare say, for the last time in my life, a few *signs* only of the deer were seen, and, as to a deer itself, I saw none.

'Mr. —— returned, accompanied by three gentlemen. They looked upon me as if I had been Washington himself, and walked to the ash tree, which I now called my own, as if in quest of a long-lost treasure. I took an axe from one of them, and cut a few chips off the bark. Still no signs were to be seen. So I cut again, until I thought it time to be cautious, and I scraped and worked away with my butcher knife until I *did* come to where my tomahawk had left an impression on the wood. We now went regularly to work, and scraped at the tree with care, until three hacks, as plain as any three notches ever were, could be seen. Mr. —— and the other gentlemen were astonished, and I must allow that I was as much surprised as pleased myself. I made affidavit of this remarkable occurrence in presence of these gentlemen. Mr. —— gained his cause. I left Green River forever, and came to where we now are; and, sir, I wish you a good night.'

Fighting Indians With Tobacco

*By John M. Peck. From 'The
Life of Daniel Boone,' 1847*

THIS slight but amusing anecdote from John M. Peck's *Life of Daniel Boone* (Little & Brown, 1847) shows Kentucky already becoming a settled country. It dates from the years of comparative quiet which followed General George Rogers Clark's punitive expedition against Chillicothe in 1782 and the peace with Great Britain the next year. According to this yarn, Boone the farmer was as resourceful as Boone the backwoodsman.

Fighting Indians With Tobacco

THOUGH no hostile attacks from Indians disturbed the settlements, still there were small parties discovered, or *signs* seen in the frontier settlements. On one occasion, about this period, four Indians came to the farm of Colonel Boone, and nearly succeeded in taking him prisoner. The particulars are given, as they were narrated by Boone himself, at the wedding of a granddaughter, a few months before his decease, and they furnish an illustration of his habitual self-possession and tact with Indians. At a short distance from his cabin, he had raised a small patch of tobacco, to supply his neighbors (for Boone never used the 'filthy weed' himself), the amount, perhaps, of one hundred and fifty hills.

As a shelter for curing it, he had built an enclosure of rails, a dozen feet in height, and covered it with cane and grass. Stalks of tobacco are usually split and strung on sticks about four feet in length. The ends of these are laid on poles, placed across the tobacco-house, and in tiers, one above the other, to the roof. Boone had fixed his temporary shelter in such a manner as to have three tiers. He had covered the lower tier, and the tobacco had become dry, when he entered the shelter for the purpose of removing the sticks to the upper tier, preparatory to gathering the remainder of the crop. He had hoisted up the sticks from the lower to the second tier, and was standing on the poles that supported it while raising the sticks to the upper tier, when four stout Indians, with guns, entered the low door and called him by name. 'Now, Boone, we got you. You no get away more. We carry you off to Chillicothe this time. You no cheat us any more.' Boone looked down upon their upturned faces, saw their loaded guns pointed at his breast, and recognizing some of his old friends, the Shawanoes, who had made him prisoner near the Blue Licks, in 1778, coolly and pleasantly responded, 'Ah! old friends! Glad to see you.' Perceiving that they manifested impatience to have him come down, he told them he was quite willing to go with them, and only begged they would wait where they were, and watch him closely, until he could finish removing his tobacco.

While parleying with them, inquiring after old acquaintances, and proposing to give them his tobacco when cured, he diverted their attention from his purpose, until he had collected together a number of sticks of dry tobacco, and so turned them as to fall between the poles directed in their faces. At the same instant, he jumped upon them with as much of the dry tobacco as he could gather in his arms, filling their mouths and eyes with its pungent dust, and, blinding and disabling them from following him, rushed out and hastened to his cabin, where he had the means of defense. Notwithstanding the narrow escape, he could not resist the temptation, after retreating some fifteen or twenty yards, to look round and see the success of his achievement. The Indians, blinded and nearly suffocated, were stretching out their hands and feeling

The Tobacco Ruse

about in different directions, calling him by name, and cursing him for a rogue, and themselves for fools. The old man, in telling the story, imitated their gestures and tones of voice with great glee.

The Hunters of Kentucky

or

Half Horse and Half Alligator

By Samuel Woodworth. From 'The American Songbag,' edited by Carl Sandburg, 1927

IN THE War of 1812 the Kentucky backwoodsman came into his own. This triumphant ditty celebrates the events of January 8, 1815, when the British made their final attack on New Orleans. Between them and the city lay a 'low log breastwork, manned by a backwoods rabble.' The rabble, composed largely of Kentuckians, was led by Old Hickory. The redcoats, under Sir Edward Pakenham, launched their attack through the early morning mist. When they were some three hundred yards from the breastwork, the fog lifted. Every 'dirty shirt' (as the British termed them, from their unbleached homespun) drew bead just above an enemy belt-plate. The slaughter was terrific. The British ranks broke, the cane stubble was heaped with bodies, Pakenham himself was killed, and the American Frontiersman realized one of the great moments in his history.

'The Hunters of Kentucky' is reprinted here, with the permission of the publishers, from *The American Songbag* by Carl Sandburg (New York: Harcourt, Brace and Company, 1927). Written by Samuel Woodworth, author of 'The Old Oaken Bucket,' it was sung in a New Orleans theater in 1822 and published in a book of songs and ballads four years later. As Sandburg's note tells us, it was also printed in Boston as a broadside, and has been heard among mountaineers, cowboys, and lumberjacks. The text is from a broadside in the Congressional Library.

The supposed boast of Pakenham (here spelled Packenham) concerning the New Orleans belles (stanza 4) has a parallel in Waldo's *Memoirs of Andrew Jackson*, 1820:

'It must crimson with a blush every Englishman ... when he finds it recorded, that an officer, the pride of England, confident of capturing one of the finest cities in America, gave it as a *countersign*, upon the day his army was to enter it — "BOOTY, and BEAUTY!!" The hard earnings of patient industry were to be ravished from the defenceless citizens, and their wives and daughters to be subjected to the diabolical lust of a full-gorged soldiery. The innocent and accomplished females of New Orleans ... were to suffer more than ten thousand deaths could inflict. ... Well may the English reader exclaim with an ancient poet — "*Quis temperet a lachrymis, talia fando*" (who can refrain from tears in relating such deeds).'

The Hunters of Kentucky

YE gentlemen and ladies fair,
   Who grace this famous city,
   Just listen if you've time to spare,
While I rehearse a ditty;
And for the opportunity
   Conceive yourselves quite lucky,
For 'tis not often that you see
   A hunter from Kentucky.
Oh Kentucky, the hunters of Kentucky!
Oh Kentucky, the hunters of Kentucky!

We are a hardy, free-born race,
   Each man to fear a stranger;
Whate'er the game we join in chase,
   Despoiling time and danger,
And if a daring foe annoys,
   Whate'er his strength and forces,
We'll show him that Kentucky boys
   Are alligator horses.
             Oh Kentucky, etc.

I s'pose you've read it in the prints,
   How Packenham attempted

Old Hickory

To make Old Hickory Jackson wince,
    But soon his scheme repented;
For we, with rifles ready cock'd,
    Thought such occasion lucky,
And soon around the gen'ral flock'd
    The hunters of Kentucky.
                Oh Kentucky, etc.

You've heard, I s'pose, how New-Orleans
    Is fam'd for wealth and beauty,
There's girls of ev'ry hue it seems,
    From snowy white to sooty.
So Packenham he made his brags,
    If he in fight was lucky,
He'd have their girls and cotton bags,
    In spite of old Kentucky.
                Oh Kentucky, etc.

But Jackson he was wide awake,
    And was not scar'd at trifles,
For well he knew what aim we take
    With our Kentucky rifles.
So he led us down to Cypress Swamp,
    The ground was low and mucky,
There stood John Bull in martial pomp
    And here was old Kentucky.
                Oh Kentucky, etc.

A bank was rais'd to hide our breasts,
    Not that we thought of dying,
But that we always like to rest,
    Unless the game is flying.

Behind it stood our little force,
    None wished it to be greater,
For ev'ry man was half a horse,
    And half an alligator.
                Oh Kentucky, etc.

They did not let our patience tire,
    Before they show'd their faces;
We did not choose to waste our fire,
    So snugly kept our places.
But when so near we saw them wink,
    We thought it time to stop 'em,
And 'twould have done you good I think,
    To see Kentuckians drop 'em.
                Oh Kentucky, etc.

They found, at last, 'twas vain to fight,
　Where *lead* was all the *booty*,
And so they wisely took to flight,
　And left *us* all our *beauty*.
And now, if danger e'er annoys,
　Remember what our trade is,
Just send for us Kentucky boys,
　And we'll protect ye, ladies.
　　　　　　　Oh Kentucky, etc.

The Captivity of Simon Kenton

From 'The Great West,'
ed. by Henry Howe, 1855

SIMON KENTON is one of the great backwoodsmen who have been overshadowed by more familiar heroes. Until 1930, when Edna Kenton published *Simon Kenton: His Life and Period* (Doubleday, Doran), there was no full-length biography of him, though his importance was recognized in many frontier annals. He was neither a practical organizer like George Rogers Clark, nor a master colonist like Boone, but a free man 'on his own hook' — a phrase, says his biographer, used over and over by his contemporaries to describe him.

Born in Virginia in 1755, he belonged, roughly, to the generation between Boone and Crockett. At sixteen, after a desperate fight over a girl, in which he thought he had killed his rival, Kenton ran away from home and drifted westward, changing his name to Simon Butler. At Fort Pitt he formed a lifelong friendship with Simon Girty, the notorious renegade, who was later to rescue him from the stake. Eventually he joined Boone as a scout, took an heroic part in the early defense of Boonesborough, and on one occasion saved the Colonel's life. In 1778 he served with General Clark in the march to Kaskaskia and later in that year crossed the Ohio on a spying expedition to Chillicothe, 'an adventure,' writes Edna Kenton, 'which, for its momentous succession of perils, transitions, and hairbreadth escapes, has not its parallel in all the adventurous annals of western border history.' The story of his capture and torture by the Indians is vividly described in *The Great West* by Henry Howe (Greenville, Tennessee, 1855), reprinted in the following pages.

After his escape, the indomitable Kenton again joined Clark and later founded Kenton Station on the northern border of Kentucky, keeping watch on the Ohio for Indian raids. He served in the War of 1812 and his last years were spent in Ohio, where he died in 1836.

The Captivity of Simon Kenton

SIMON KENTON, one of the most noted pioneers of the West, was born in Virginia, in 1755. He was over six feet in stature, erect, graceful, and of uncommon strength, endurance, and agility. His complexion and hair were light, and his soft, grayish-blue eye was lighted up by a bewitching, fascinating smile. He was frank, generous and confiding to a fault, and was more interested in doing a kindness to others than in serving himself. When enraged, his glance was withering. To give full account of his adventures would fill a volume. A few anecdotes must answer.

In September, 1778, Kenton, Montgomery, and Clarke left the stations, in Kentucky, to obtain horses from the Indians. They crossed the Ohio, and proceeded cautiously to the Indian Village, on the site of Oldtown, near the site of Chillicothe. They caught seven horses, and rapidly retreated to the Ohio; but the wind blowing almost a hurricane, made the river so rough that they could not induce their horses to take to the water. The next day, they were come up with by the Indians in pursuit. The whites happened, at the moment, to be separated. Kenton, judging the boldest course to be the safest, very deliberately took aim at the foremost Indian. His gun flashed in the pan.

He then retreated. The Indians pursued on horseback. In his retreat, he passed through a piece of land where a storm had torn up a great part of the timber. The fallen trees afforded him some advantage of the Indians in the race, as they were on horseback and he on foot. The Indian force divided; some rode on one side of the fallen timber, and some on the other. Just as he emerged from the fallen timber, at the foot of the hill, one of the Indians met him on horseback, and boldly rode up to him, jumped off his horse and rushed at him with his tomahawk. Kenton, concluding a gun-barrel as good a weapon of defense as a tomahawk, drew back his gun to strike the Indian before him. At that instant, another Indian, who, unperceived by Kenton, had slipped up behind him, clasped him in his arms. Being now overpowered by numbers, further resistance was useless — he surrendered. While the Indians were binding Kenton with tugs, Montgomery came in view, and fired at the Indians, but missed his mark. Montgomery fled on foot. Some of the Indians pursued, shot at and missed him; a second fire was made, and Montgomery fell. The Indians soon returned to Kenton, shaking at him Montgomery's bloody scalp. Clarke, Kenton's other companion, escaped.

The horrors of his captivity during nine months among the Indians may be briefly enumerated, but they cannot be described. The sufferings of his body may be recounted, but the anguish of his mind, the internal torments of spirit, none but himself could know.

The first regular torture was the hellish one of Mazeppa. He was securely bound, hand and foot, upon the back of an unbroken horse, which plunged furiously through the forest, through thickets, briers, and brush, vainly endeavoring to rid himself of the unwelcome rider on his back, until completely exhausted. By this time Kenton had been bruised, lacerated, scratched, and mangled, until life itself was nearly extinct, while his sufferings had

afforded the most unbounded ecstasies of mirth to his savage captors. This, however, was only a prelude to subsequent sufferings.

Upon the route to the Indian towns, for the greater security of their prisoner the savages bound him securely, with his body extended upon the ground, and each foot and hand tied to a stake or sapling; and to preclude the possibility of escape, a young sapling was laid across his breast, having its extremities well secured to the ground, while a rope secured his neck to another sapling. In this condition, nearly naked, and exposed to swarms of gnats and mosquitoes, he was compelled to spend the tedious night upon the cold ground, exposed to the chilling dews of autumn.

On the third day, at noon, he was within one mile of old Chillicothe, the present site of Frankfort, where he was detained in confinement until the next day. Toward evening, curiosity had brought hundreds, of all sexes and conditions, to view the great Kentuckian. Their satisfaction at his wretched condition was evinced by numerous grunts, kicks, blows, and stripes, inflicted amid applauding yells, dancing, and every demonstration of savage indignation.

This, however, was only a prelude to a more energetic mode of torture the next day, in which the whole village were to be partakers. The torture of a prisoner is a school for the young warrior, to stir up his hatred for their white enemies, and keep alive the fire of revenge, while it affords sport and mirth to gratify the vindictive rage of bereaved mothers and relatives, by participating in the infliction of the agonies which he is compelled to suffer.

Running the gantlet was the torture of the next day, when nearly three hundred Indians, of both sexes and all ages, were assembled for the savage festival.

The ceremony commenced. Kenton, nearly naked, and freed from his bonds, was produced as the victim of the ceremony. The Indians were ranged in two parallel lines, about six feet apart, all armed with sticks, hickory rods, whips, and other means of inflicting pain. Between these lines, for more than half a mile, to the village, the wretched prisoner was doomed to run for his life, exposed to such injury as his tormentors could inflict as he passed. If he succeeded in reaching the council-house alive, it would prove an asylum to him for the present. At a given signal, Kenton started in the perilous race. Exerting his utmost strength and activity, he passed swiftly along the line, receiving numerous blows, stripes, buffets, and wounds, until he approached the town, near which he saw an Indian leisurely awaiting his advance with a drawn knife in his hand, intent upon his death.

To avoid him, he instantly broke through the line, and made his rapid way toward the council-house, pursued by the promiscuous crowd, whooping and yelling like infernal furies at his heels. Entering the town in advance of his pursuers, just as he had supposed the council-house within his reach, an Indian was perceived leisurely approaching him, with his blanket wrapped around him; but suddenly he threw off his blanket, and sprang upon Kenton as he advanced. Exhausted with fatigue and wounds, he was thrown to the ground, and in a moment he was beset with crowds, eager to strip him, and to inflict upon him each the kick or blow which had been avoided by breaking through the line. Here, beaten, kicked, and scourged until he was nearly lifeless, he was left to die.

A few hours afterward, having partially revived, he was supplied with food and water, and was suffered to recuperate for a few days, until he was able to attend at the council-house and receive the announcement of his final doom.

After a violent discussion, the council, by a large majority, determined that he should be made a public sacrifice to the vengeance of the nation; and the decision was announced by a burst of savage joy, with yells and shouts which made the welkin ring. The place of execution was

Wappatomica, the present site of Zanesfield, in Logan County, Ohio. On his route to this place, he was taken through Pickaway and Mackacheck on the Scioto, where he was again compelled to undergo the torture of the gantlet, and was scourged through the line. At this place, smarting under his wounds and bruises, he was detained several days, in order that he might recuperate preparatory to his march to Wappatomica. At length, being carelessly guarded, he determined, if possible, to make his escape from the impending doom. In this attempt he had proceeded two miles from the place of confinement, when he was met by two Indians on horseback, who in a brutal manner drove him back to the village. The last ray of hope had now expired, and, loathing a life of continual suffering, he in despair resigned himself to his fate.

His late attempt to escape had brought upon him a repetition of savage torture which had well-nigh closed his sufferings forever, and he verily believed himself a 'God-forsaken wretch.' Taken to a neighboring creek, he was thrown in and dragged through mud and water, and submerged repeatedly, until life was nearly extinct, when he was again left in a dying state; but the constitutional vigor within him revived, and a few days afterward he was taken to Wappatomica for execution. At Wappatomica he first saw, at a British trading-post, his old friend Simon Girty, who had become a renegade, in all the glory of his Indian life, surrounded by swarms of Indians, who had come to view the doomed prisoner and to witness his torture. Yet Girty suspected not the presence of his old acquaintance at Fort Pitt. Although well acquainted with Kenton only a few years before, his present mangled condition and his blackened face left no traces of recognition in

Running the Gantlet

Girty's mind. Looking upon him as a doomed victim, beyond the reach of pity or hope, he could view him only as the victim of sacrifice; but so soon as Kenton succeeded in making himself known to Girty, the hard heart of the latter at once relented, and sympathizing with his miser. able condition and still more horrid doom, he resolved to make an effort for his release. His whole personal influence, and his eloquence, no less than his intrigue, were put in requisition for the safety of his fallen friend. He portrayed in strong language the policy of preserving the life of the prisoner, and the advantage which might accrue to the Indians from the possession of one so intimately acquainted with all the white settlements. For a time Girty's eloquence prevailed, and a respite was granted; but suspicions arose, and he was again summoned before the council. The death of Kenton was again decreed. Again the influence of Girty prevailed, and through finesse he accomplished a further respite, together with a removal of the prisoner to Sandusky.

Here again the council decreed his death, and again he was compelled to submit to the terrors of the gantlet, preliminary to his execution. Still Girty did not relax his efforts. Despairing of his own influence with the council, he secured the aid and influence of Logan, 'the friend of white men.' Logan interceded with Captain Drouillard, a British officer, and procured through him the offer of a liberal ransom to the vindictive savages for the life of the prisoner. Captain Drouillard met the council, and urged the great advantage such a prisoner would be to the commandant at Detroit, in procuring from him such information as would greatly facilitate his future operations against the rebel colonies. At the same time, appealing to their avarice, he suggested that the ransom would be proportionate to the value of the prisoner.

Drouillard guaranteed the ransom of one hundred dollars for his delivery, and Kenton was given to him in charge for the commandant at Detroit. As soon as his mind was out of suspense, his robust constitution and iron frame recovered from the severe treatment which they had undergone. Kenton passed the winter and spring at Detroit. Among the prisoners were Captain Nathan Bullit and Jesse Coffer. They had the liberty of the town, and could stroll about at pleasure.

With these two men, Kenton began to meditate an escape. They had frequent conferences on the subject; but the enterprise was almost too appalling for even these hardy, enterprising pioneers. If they should make this bold push, they would have to travel nearly four hundred miles through the Indian country, where they would be exposed to death by starvation, by flood, by the tomahawk, or to capture, almost at every step. But the longer they brooded over the enterprise, the stronger their resolutions grew to make the attempt. They could make no movement to procure arms, ammunition, or provision without exciting suspicion; and should they be once suspected they would be immediately confined. In this situation, they could only brood over their wished flight in secret and in silence. Kenton was a fine-looking man, with a dignified and manly deportment, and a soft, pleasing voice, and was, everywhere he went, a favorite among the ladies. A Mrs. Harvey, the wife of an Indian trader, had treated him with particular respect ever since he came to Detroit, and he concluded if he could engage this lady as a confidante, by her assistance and countenance, ways

and means could be prepared to aid them in their meditated flight. Kenton approached Mrs. Harvey on this
delicate and interesting subject, with as much trepidation
and coyness as ever maiden was approached in a love
affair. The great difficulty with Kenton was to get the
subject opened with Mrs. Harvey. If she should reject his
suit and betray his intentions, all his fond hopes would be
at once blasted. However, at length he concluded to trust
this lady with the scheme of his meditated flight, and the
part he wished her to act for him. He watched an opportunity to have a private interview with Mrs. Harvey; an
opportunity soon offered, and he, without disguise or hesi-
tation, in full confidence informed her of his intention, and
requested her aid and secrecy. She appeared at first astonished at his proposal, and observed that it was not in her
power to afford him any aid. Kenton told her he did not
expect or wish her to be at any expense on their account —
that they had a little money for which they had labored,
and that they wished her to be their agent to purchase such
articles as would be necessary for them in their flight; that
if they should go to purchasing, it would create suspicion,
but that she could aid them in this way without creating
any suspicion; and if she would be their friend, they had
no doubt they could effect their escape. This appeal, from
such a fine-looking man as Kenton, was irresistible. There
was something pleasing in being the selected confidante of
such a man; and the lady, though a little coy at first, surrendered at discretion. After a few chit-chats, she entered
into the views of Kenton with as much earnestness and
enthusiasm as if she had been his sister. She began to col-
lect and conceal such articles as might be necessary in the
journey — powder, lead, moccasins, and dried beef were

procured in small quantities, and concealed in a hollow tree some distance out of town. Guns were still wanting, and it would not do for a lady to trade in them. Mr. Harvey had an excellent fowling-piece, if nothing better should offer, that she said should be at their service. They had now everything that they expected to take with them in their flight ready, except guns.

At length the third day of June, 1779, came, and a large concourse of Indians were in the town engaged in a drunken frolic; they had stacked their guns near Mrs. Harvey's house; as soon as it was dark, Mrs. Harvey went quietly to where the Indians' guns were stacked, and selected the three best-looking rifles, carried them into her garden, and concealed them in a patch of peas. She next went privately to Kenton's lodging, and conveyed to him the intelligence where she had hid the Indians' guns. She told him she would place a ladder at the back of the garden (it was picketed), and that he could come in and get the guns. No time was to be lost; Kenton conveyed the good news he had from Mrs. Harvey to his companions, who received the tidings in ecstasies of joy; they felt as if they were already at home. It was a dark night; Kenton, Bullit, and Coffer gathered up their little all and pushed to Mrs. Harvey's garden. There they found the ladder; Kenton mounted over, drew the ladder over after him, went to the pea-patch, found Mrs. Harvey sitting by the guns; she handed him the rifles, gave him a friendly shake of the hand, and bid him a safe journey to his friends and countrymen.

The Defense of Boonesborough

The Mule-Humans

By Percy MacKaye. From 'Tall Tales of the Kentucky Mountains,' 1926

U NLIKE most of the stories in this book, 'The Mule-
Humans' does not deal with a specific pioneer hero.
It is a perfect example of the humorous 'tall tale,'
rendered in the authentic spoken idiom of one of the last sur-
viving corners of the American Frontier. It ranks with the
best of the priceless legends which Mr. MacKaye has re-created
from the heart of the Kentucky Mountains, as Washington
Irving and Joel Chandler Harris reclaimed for posterity the
Dutch lore of the Catskill Mountains and the Negro lore of
the Southern Lowlands. In this locale of the Kentucky Ridges
(to quote Mr. MacKaye's Introduction), 'the creek-beds are
alive with an ancient leisure, voluble with antic tongues in the
smoky log cabins, where Aesop and Chaucer and Munchausen
still sit anonymous by the fireside and spin their timeless lore.'

This tale, 'The Mule-Humans,'[1] is here reprinted, for inclusion in this volume only, by permission of the author, from his
book, *Tall Tales of the Kentucky Mountains*, which is one of
Mr. MacKaye's *Kentucky Mountain Cycle* of volumes con-
cerned with themes of the legendary lore of that mountain
region, written in the native folk-speech of the Southern
Appalachians.

The Mule-Humans

CHILDERS, don't never git to squabblin' on a' amber-day. Don't resk hit. Hit mought lead ye in jepparty, where ye wouldn't know your own face in a mirrer-glass.

What-all is a' amber-day? Hain't you larned your almanack scriptures yit? A' amber-day is a pizen day. Hit's a day that one ongodless word will spell-charm your nearest kin so's you'd take him for the Deevil hisself. Old Horny sprinkled a handful o' them days through the year, like rat-pizened ears in a corn-crib, for fool critters to nibble at an' shed the skins they was borned in.

No-o, hit don't plumb kill ye. Only jist ef ye wish the wrong wish, or speak the wrong word, the Deevil he kin cross-breed ye to a dumb brute in one bat of his eye. That's why me an' my ole woman allers keeps our mouth shet amber-days. We don't aim to git us in no sech a scrape as Godsey Scrorse done with his ole woman, Mondie.

What-a-way did they done? Ax me no axin's, an' I'll fib ye no fairy-tales. Hit were so fashion:

Years ago yander, Godsey Scrorse war a' up-creek

neebor o' mine. Him an' Mondie, his wife, they lived in a lonesome holler.

He were a good, lousy, lay-around, patientablest feller, Godsey; but she were pernickety as a pea-hen: gibble-gabble an' peck from day-up till dark.

Well, one fall o' the year, hit comin' night-down, I war passin' of their cabin, an' I hears her thar inside brash-whackin' at him. So I stops an' listens.

'Git your dad-burned big feet offen my toes, trompin' all over me! Cain't never give me room to set easy an' stretch! Allers jammin' on me! Nothin' but clopper-legs an' hoofs, you hain't! God-a-mighty knows you ain't nothin' but a mule-brute from the middle down — dad-bust ye!'

'An' you — from the neck up, ole woman!' he answers her.

'Yea, I wisht you *was* a saddle-critter,' she hollers. 'I'd ride ye down to Solomon Shell's an' swap ye fer his gang o' shoats.'

'An' I'd trade *you* fer his ole sow!' he hollers back.

Well, I'd heerd enough. 'Pore ole Godsey is shore losin' his patience,' thinks I, 'an' 'taint to wonder.' An' I goes on home, about three mile down trail.

So thar I was a-settin' in the yard, tippin' snuff ter-baccy, an' hit darkin' outdoors. My ole woman she were pokin' the supper-pot, an' kindly she raised up an' says sobersome:

'Sol,' she says, 'what time is hit?'

'Fall o' the year,' says I, ''most time fer supper.'

'Quit triflin' me,' she says. 'Hit's amber-day.'

An' jist then I hears stones clickin' on the trail, an' somebody hollers out in a quare, grummy voice:

'Hey, Solomon! Solomon Shell!'

Lorsy me! I looks up, an' thar, high over the palin's, I sees a shaddersome haid peekin' down the face of Godsey Scrorse. All scrooged up hit were, goshawful, an' his mouth gappin', like he seen a hant. Well, chilluns, that turned my belly over.

'Good evenin', Godsey,' I says. 'Air you ridin'?'

'No-o,' he says, 'I's leggin' hit.'

'How did ye clumb up thar, that high?' I axes.

'I hain't clumb up,' he answers me, the same quare noise.

'Hain't ye?' says I. 'Well, come in, anyhow, an' take a cheer.'

'I cain't come in,' says he, 'an' I cain't take a cheer, never no more.'

'Why-fer no?' says I, in the pit o' my belly.

'My bottom hain't balanced right,' says he. 'Come out an' prospect hit.'

Well, rounders, out I goes through the palin' gate, an' thar in the gloomin' I sees the quarest six-limbdest critter sence Joshuay tuck to raisin' horse flesh. The top half of hit — arms, chist, an' haid — was shore 'nough Godsey Scrorse hisself. He were chawin' terbaccy, his hat dipped on his left eye, an' one gallus was holdin' up his pants, which only they wasn't ary legs in 'em. Stid o' that, the impty breeches was danglin' thar split-busted, like a bib an' tucker, down over the breast-front of a thunderin'-gret, leggy mule-critter, which hit's withers sprung behind from the small o' Godsey's back. So the bottom half of the hull goll machine were a quadrupeed, which his piebald cruppers was switchin' his hocks with a ratsy tail.

'Lordamassy!' I says. 'If ye're aimin' to ride, Godsey, you's shore pitched for'ard in the saddle. But you's plumb right about your bottom never needin' a cheer ag'in. How-all did you git grafted with that-thar mule-rump?'

Poor Godsey jist rubbed his hind fetlocks an' pawed dirt with one for'ard hoof, an' he answers:

'Hit's plain weetchery!'

'No, 'tain't,' I says; 'hit's pizen. Ye're amber-day pizened. Somebody must 'a' ben cussin' you in angry fer Old Horny to overhear hit.'

'Yea,' he says; 'hit were Mondie, my ole woman. She mule-cussed me from the middle down, an' I cussed her back ag'in, from the neck up. For the love o' neebors, Sol, will ye holp us git the spell off?'

'How kin I, Godsey?'

'Mondie wants me to ax ye — will ye trade your gang o' shoats for this-yere mule-brute. That's our one-only chanct to git shet of hit, she says.'

'Whar's the rightly haid that goes with hit?' says I.

'To home with Mondie,' says he. 'Hit were too shame-bashed to come along with the laigs. Git up on behind, an' I'll tote ye home, to look her over.'

So upsy I climbs on the middle of his ridge-bone, which hit nigh splitted me in the fork, an' he retches one hand to break him a hazel switch, an' whops hisself in the shanks, an' hollers out, 'Co-oop, Godsey!' an' away I rides him bareback, splashin' the crick ford.

Well, of all the goll-durned night-riders, us'ns was the quarest twins the moon ever riz on. I grabbed one busted gallus for a bridle-rein, but fust time I jerked hit, he turned his haid round sorreful an' says:

'Sol,' he says, 'I'd give ten bucks fer to have your laigs in my pants.'

Nary nuther word he spoke for a long piece o' trail, but

'Co-oop, Godsey!'

he spit moughty reg'lar. Arter that I hadn't the sand fer
to bridle-steer him ag'in. So I jist aidged for'ard on his
withers, an' clipped both arms round his waist, to ease my
own bacon behind.

A whisk o' rain come peltin' from the verge o' the moon.
Clob-clopperty pore Godsey splashed his hoofs in the trail-
puddles. Onc't he retched his hand in the poke of his
impty pants fer a chunk o' baccy. He chawed a quid o'
that, which hit 'peared to live'-up his back-laigs, fer he
trotted right smart till Preachin' Charlie's palin's.

Charlie war jist packin' a yoke o' full pails from his
water spring, turnin' to ope his gate.

'Retch me up a drink, Preacher, will ye?' calls Godsey,
puffin'. 'This-here haulin' ole Sol uphill has wheezed me
dry.'

Preachin' Charlie give one look.

'Valley o' the shadder!' he yells, an' he clares that gate
same's a wild duck — the spilt pails swingin' out from his
yoke like wing-paddles. Half a mile back, I could hear
him hollerin' to God yit thar.

Next cabin us passed was Fiddler John's. An' thar he
hisself was a-settin' on a gum-stump, sawin' of his fiddle
in the face o' the moon. His own face war puckered up,
losty in his music.

Godsey stopped, fore an' aft.

'Heigh, John Fiddler,' he cuts in, 'kin you liquor me?
I's lost my britch-bottle.'

Old Fiddler pauses his fiddlestick plumb in the air, an'
he stares at us'ns a hull minute without winkin'.

'Double!' he says, drappin' his voice. 'Nay, good feller!
I hain't tetched a dram. In the Three Highest, I hain't!
But if you-all is a horse-critter of Rivelation, you's the

first mule-human ever I heerd quoted in Scriptur'. As fer britch-sperrits, I cain't give ye none from a bottle, but I kin from a fiddle-box.'

Right thar then he struck up an' sawed sech a dodghasted four-leggy reel that hit set Godsey high steppin', all fours, nigh pitchin' me off, whilst he galloped Injundivvles 'most home afore slackin'. Lather drippin' he was, all over, belly an' back frothin' white scum, an' me settin' in the suds bath. Well, I curried him off, best I could, with his pants legs, till lastly us cantered up to his own cabin door. An' thar was a-settin' his ole woman, rockin' of herself, with a bed-kivver throwed over her haid.

'Mondie,' he hollers, 'here's Sol. He wants the haid to go with the laigs afore he'll trade with us.'

Sodom and Gomorrah! what a bray-squawlin' she let out then!

'Hee-honker! — Hee-honker! — Hee-honker!'

An' thar she poked her long mule-muzzle outen the bed-kivver, an' her jaws gap-open a foot wide, stuck full o' gret grinders like a corn mill.

Chilluns, that drapped me to the ground!

'The pore dumb critter!' says Godsey. 'That's the only last gab-language left in her, poor Mondie!'

Then Mondie she threwed off the bed-kivver, an' riz up on the top doorstep. Yea! Fer to see that leetle woman-critter balancin' her gret mule head-piece, big's a barrel keg, I shore wagered hit 'ud topple her legs-up! But thar she stood wagglin' of her long, p'inted ears, an' retchin' her both arms to Godsey.

Hit were a sight pitiful. The gret teardraps, round as oak galls, come oozin' outen her muly pop-eyes, rollin' down off her nozzle, which she tried fer to blow hit dry with her apron, but jist only drinched the cabin-yard.

An' thar come Godsey tromplin' the flower-patch, all four hoofs diggin' up the mud like mattocks, an' tuck Mondie in his arms, an' he holds her mule-haid tilted how hit ought to jine on to his mule underpinnin's, so's to sample one hull-complete mule-critter fer the swap bargain.

'Thar, Sol,' he says, 'will ye trade in your ole sow for the hull consarn?'

'Dadfetch me, I won't!' says I. 'The archeetecture don't jine. Thar's one joist missin' from the middle up.'

'Yis, God holp us!' he groans. 'The middlin's is lost out. I jist only cussed her neck-up'ards.'

Well, at that, Mondie busts out hee-honkin' ag'in fit to kill; but Godsey pats her nozzle soothey-like, an' he hollers down one ear like a cornycopee trumpet: 'Co-oop, Mondie gal! I'll stick by ye, haids or tails.'

Then he turns to me, plumb piteous, an' says:

'Solomon,' he says, 'have a heart! How's we to git traded of this amber-day mule withouten you to holp us swap the spell off?'

'Godsey,' I says, 'listen of me. I wouldn't swap my ole sow, Chinkapin, for a' army of amber-day mules: no, nor her shoat babies nuther. All the same, I ain't a feller not to holp my neebors out. You an' Mondie is pizened. Now, they's jist only one way I knows to git shet of amber-day pizen.'

'In the fear o' God, what is hit?' he axes.

'You's said hit,' I answers. 'Hit's the fear o' God hitself. Hit's a dose o' Scriptur'. There hain't no other medicine kin purge ye of amber-day pizen. Air ye ready to swaller hit now?'

'Yis, shorely,' he says.

'Then jist hand me yan hazel ridin'-switch ye got thar.'

'The switch?' he says, side-steppin' with his hind-laigs, while he retched hit to me. 'But what-all of a dose air ye aimin' to give us?'

'I's aimin' to dose ye with Balaam's medicine: *Numbers*, Two and Twenty, Twenty-seven to Twenty-nine:

' *"And Balaam's anger hit were kindled an' he smote the ass with a staff."* '

'Whoa, thar!' hollers Godsey to his hinter parts, which was buck-humpin' to let fly a double-backer. 'Not *twenty-nine* licks, Sol!'

But I quoted straight on, calm's a cow-cumber:

' *"And the Lord opened the mouth of the ass, an' she says unto Balaam: What have I done unto thee, she says, that thou hast smitten me these-yere three times?"* '

'Hold yit!' spoke Godsey ag'in. 'Three doses, is hit? An' jist only *her* swallers 'em? — Yea, now, that ain't so worse!'

So then Godsey's spine comminced to slack rope a leetle, but mine jest gingered, a-stirrin' that Scriptur'-dose:

' *"An' Balaam says unto the ass: Because thou hast mocked me, he says!"* —

'Thar, neebors! That's your Bible text: now follers your sarmon.'

So I raises that ridin'-switch an' spits on hit.

That skeert poor Mondie flap-jawed. She honked one last *hee-honker* an' rammed a black eye in Godsey, kissin' his hat off blubberin'.

But I never scringes. I jist whistles that hazel switch in the air, an' I larrups each of 'em three licks, haid-piece an' cruppers.

That settled hit.

Yea, sirs, that druv the pizen plumb out! Godsey's own legs was in his pants ag'in, an' thar stood Mondie puggin' up her red back-haars, a-snufflin' of her leetle nose, an' grinnin' at him.

As fer that amber-day Mule-Deevil, hit cut loost an' high-jumped clare over Godsey's palin's, me throwin' the hazel switch after. Last thing I seed of hit, loamin' ag'in the moon, the critter war raisin' one hoof, tryin' to tie a knot in the witch-stick, fer to splice hit's haid on. An' if yan hoof warn't *cloved* ... ? .!

'Thar, Mondie,' I says, moughty awfulsome, 'you's clean purged fer *this* time, an' you kin thank that dose o' Scriptur' fer your purty face ag'in. But hinceforthly, mind ye ponder on the ass what mocked Balaam! An', Godsey, don't ye never git to treadin' on your ole woman's toes no more!'

Then Mondie sassed up piert an' says:

'Hit jist pime-blank proves what I war callin' of him. God-a-mighty knows how Godsey hain't nothin' but a dadburned critter of a ole mu——'

'Choke off, thar!' hollers Godsey. 'Dud-drattle ye! — Hit's amber-day yit!'

Now, neebors, I axes ye: *kin* humans git cured o' mule-cussidness?

Lewis Weitzel, Indian Hunter

By Florus B. Plimpton. From 'The Back-Woodsmen,' ed. by Walter W. Spooner, 1883

THE typical frontiersman killed savages cold-bloodedly and casually. Lewis Weitzel (Wetzel, Whetzel) slaughtered them all his life with single-minded fury. His passion dated from childhood. He was born near Wheeling, Ohio, in the 1760's, the second of four sons. When he was thirteen years old, Indians attacked the Weitzel home, killed his father, and captured Lewis and a younger brother. They escaped and, on growing up, the four brothers 'took a solemn oath never to make peace with the Indians while they had strength to wield a tomahawk or sight to draw a bead.' Hunting savages became their favorite sport and regular business. Of the four brothers, Lewis made the largest bag. He did not go in for tall talk, but he would suffer any hardship and danger for an Indian scalp. As recounted in Blair and Meine's life of Fink, Weitzel would now and then, when thawed with whiskey, tell of his exploits — his killing three savages in a running fight, loading and firing as he ran; or the unlucky adventure when, said he, 'I treed four Injuns, but one got away.'

Weitzel's appearance was apparently in keeping with his profession. 'He was about five feet nine inches in height, very broad-shouldered and full-breasted. His complexion was dark and swarthy as an Indian's, and his face pitted with the smallpox. His hair, of which he was very careful, reached, when combed out, to the calves of his legs; his eyes were remarkably black, and, when excited — which was easily done — they would sparkle with such a vindictive glance as almost to curdle the blood of the beholder.' (Howe, *The Great West.*)

The following poem shows how blithe and pretty a hard-bitten, pockmarked roughneck can appear, once the romantic view of the frontier is established. In ballad style, it recounts a Robin Hood incident with greensward, stag, and all the trappings. This poem appeared in *The Back-Woodsmen, or Tales of the Borders,* edited by Walter W. Spooner, 1883.

Lewis Weitzel
Indian Hunter

STOUT–HEARTED Lewis Weitzel
   Rides down the river shore,
   The wilderness behind him,
The wilderness before.

He rides in the cool of morning,
   Humming a dear old tune,
Into the heart of the greenwood,
   Into the heart of June.

He needs no guide in the forest
   More than the hunter bees;
His guides are the cool green mosses
   To the northward of the trees.

Nor fears he the foe whose footstep
   Is light as the summer air —
The tomahawk hangs in his shirt-belt,
   The scalp-knife glitters there!

The stealthy Wyandots tremble,
   And speak his name with fear,

For his aim is sharp and deadly,
 And his rifle's ring is clear.

So, pleasantly rides he onward,
 Pausing to hear the stroke
Of the settler's axe in the forest,
 Or the crash of a falling oak.

Pausing at times to gather
 The wild fruit overhead
(For in this rarest of June days
 The service-berries are red);

And as he grasps the full boughs
 To bend them down amain,
The dew and the blushing berries
 Fall like an April rain.

The partridge drums on the dry oak,
   The croaking corby caws,
The blackbird sings in the spice-bush,
   The robin in the haws;

And, as they chatter and twitter,
   The wild birds seem to say,
'Do not harm us, good Lewis,
   And you shall have luck today.'

So, pleasantly rides he onward,
   'Til the shadows mark the noon,
Into the leafy greenwood,
   Into the heart of June.

Now, speed thee on, good Lewis,
   For the sultry sun goes down,
The hillside shadows lengthen,
   And the eastern sky is brown.

Now, speed thee where the river
   Creeps slow in the coverts cool,
And the lilies nod their white bells
   By the margin of the pool.

He crosses the silver Kaska
   With its chestnut-covered hills,
And the fetlocks of his roan steed
   Are wet in a hundred rills.

'And there,' he cries in transport,
   'The alders greenest grow,

Where the wild stag comes for water,
  And her young fawn leads the doe.'

Grasping his trusty rifle,
  He whistles his dog behind,
Then stretches his finger upward
  To know how sets the wind.

Oh! steady grows the strong arm,
  And the hunter's dark eye keen,
As he sees the branching antlers
  Through alder thickets green.

A sharp, clear ring through the greenwood,
  And with mighty leap and bound,
The pride of the Western forest
  Lies bleeding on the ground.

Then out from the leafy shadow
  A stalwart hunter springs,
And his unsheathed scalp-knife glittering
  Against his rifle rings.

'And who art thou,' quoth Lewis,
  'That com'st 'twixt me and mine?'
And his cheek is flushed with anger,
  As a Bacchant's flushed with wine.

'What boots that to thy purpose?'
  The stranger hot replies;
'My rifle marked it living,
  And mine, when dead, the prize.'

Lewis Weitzel

Then with sinewy arms they grapple,
  Like giants fierce in brawls,
Till stretched along the greensward
  The humbled hunter falls.

Upspringing like a panther,
  He cries, in wrath and pride,
'Though your arms may be the stronger,
  Our rifles shall decide.'

'Stay, stranger,' quoth good Lewis,
  'The chances are not even;
Who challenges my rifle
  Should be at peace with heaven.

'Now take this rod of alder,
  Set it by yonder tree
A hundred yards beyond me,
  And wait you there and see;

'For he who dares such peril
  But lightly holds his breath —
May his unshrived soul be ready
  To welcome sudden death.'

So the stranger takes the alder,
  And wondering stands to view,
While Weitzel's aim grows steady,
  And he cuts the rod in two.

'By Heaven!' exclaims the stranger,
  'One only, far or nigh,

Hath arms like the lithe young ash tree,
　Or half so keen an eye;

'And that is Lewis Weitzel.'
　Quoth Lewis, 'Here he stands.'
So they speak in gentler manner,
　And clasp their friendly hands.

Then talk the mighty hunters
　Till the summer dew descends,
And they who met as foemen
　Ride out of the greenwood friends; —

Ride out of the leafy greenwood
　As rises the yellow moon,
And the purple hills lie pleasantly
　In the softened air of June.

Davy Crockett Hunts Bear

From the 'Life of David Crockett,' by Himself, 1834

THOUGH Daniel Boone may symbolize the sterling virtues of the hard frontier life, Davy Crockett is the backwoodsman's own hero. He was a crack shot, fighter, and scout; a boisterous practical joker with a grin that would strip the bark off a knothole; a ring-tailed roarer who could whip his weight in wildcats. Renowned as both hunter and politician, he became a national figure long before the publication of the 'autobiography,' in which he admitted that 'obscure as I am, my name is making considerable deal of fuss in the world.' 'I can't tell why it is,' he goes on modestly, 'nor in what it is to end.' It was to end in a glorious cycle of tall tales and poetic legends, with Crockett as a demigod, riding the lightning and shooting holes through the moon.

David Crockett was born in Tennessee in 1786. He had little schooling and, in characteristic frontier fashion, boasted of the fact. 'As for grammer, it's pretty much a thing of nothing at last, after all the fuss that's made about it.... Big men have more important matters to attend to than crossing their *t*'s, and dotting their *i*'s, and such like small things.' Already an expert rifleman, he served under Andrew Jackson in the Creek War of 1813–14; in 1821 he was elected to the legislature, although wholly ignorant of public affairs. All this time he was drifting westward until he had reached the extreme western part of Tennessee, near the junction of the Obion and Mississippi Rivers. This country is the scene of the classic bear hunts narrated in the following pages, which are reprinted from 'A Narrative of the LIFE OF DAVID CROCKETT, of the State of Tennessee, Written by Himself, Philadelphia and Boston, 1834.' How far this is his own story cannot be said, 'But,' to quote Crockett's own words, 'just read for yourself, and my ears for a heel tap, if before you get through you don't say, with many a good-natured smile and hearty laugh, "This is truly the very thing itself — the exact image of its Author, DAVID CROCKETT."'

Davy Crockett Hunts Bear

IN THE morning I left my son at the camp, and we started on towards the harricane; and when we had went about a mile, we started a very large bear, but we got along mighty slow on account of the cracks in the earth occasioned by the earthquakes. We, however, made out to keep in hearing of the dogs for about three miles, and then we come to the harricane. Here we had to quit our horses, as old Nick himself couldn't have got through it without sneaking it along in the form that he put on, to make a fool of our old grandmother Eve. By this time several of my dogs had got tired and come back; but we went ahead on foot for some little time in the harricane, when we met a bear coming straight to us, and not more than twenty or thirty yards off. I started my tired dogs after him, and McDaniel pursued them, and I went on to where my other dogs were. I had seen the track of the bear they were after, and I knowed he was a screamer. I followed on to about the middle of the harricane; but my dogs pursued him so close, that they made him climb an old stump about twenty feet high. I got in shooting distance of him and fired, but I was all over in such a flutter from fatigue and running, that I couldn't hold steady; but, however, I broke his shoulder, and he fell. I run up and loaded my gun as quick as possible, and shot him again and killed him. When I went to take out my knife to butcher him, I found I had lost it in coming through the harricane. The vines and briers was so thick that I would sometimes have to get down and crawl like a varment to get through at all; and a vine had, as I supposed, caught in the handle and pulled it out. While I was standing and studying what to do, my friend came to me. He had followed my trail through the harricane, and had found my knife, which was mighty good news to me; as a hunter hates the worst in the world to lose a good dog, or any part of his hunting-tools. I now left McDaniel to butcher the bear, and I went after our horses, and brought them as near as the nature of the case would allow. I then took our bags, and went back to where he was; and when we had skin'd the bear, we fleeced off the fat and carried it to our horses at several loads. We then packed it up on our horses, and had a heavy pack of it on each one. We now started and went on till about sunset, when I concluded we must be near our camp; so I hollered and my son answered me, and we moved on in the direction to the camp. We had gone but a little way when I heard my dogs make a warm start again; and I jumped down from my horse and gave him up to my friend, and told him I would follow them. He went on to the camp, and I went ahead after my dogs with all my might for a considerable distance, till at last night came on. The woods were very rough and hilly, and all covered over with cane.

I now was compel'd to move on more slowly; and was frequently falling over logs, and into the cracks made by the earthquakes, so that I was very much afraid I would break my gun. However, I went on about three miles,

A Bear Hunt

when I came to a good big creek, which I waded. It was very cold, and the creek was about knee-deep; but I felt no great inconvenience from it just then, as I was all over wet with sweat from running, and I felt hot enough. After I got over this creek and out of the cane, which was very thick on all our creeks, I listened for my dogs. I found they had either treed or brought the bear to a stop, as they continued barking in the same place. I pushed on as near in the direction to the noise as I could, till I found the hill was too steep for me to climb, and so I backed and went down the creek some distance till I came to a hollow, and then took up that, till I come to a place where I could climb up the hill. It was mighty dark, and was difficult to see my way or anything else. When I got up the hill, I found I had passed the dogs; and so I turned and went to them. I found, when I got there, they had treed the bear in a large forked poplar, and it was setting in the fork.

I could see the lump, but not plain enough to shoot with any certainty, as there was no moonlight; and so I set in to hunting for some dry brush to make me a light; but I could find none; though I could find that the ground was torn mightily to pieces by the cracks.

At last I thought I could shoot by guess, and kill him; so I pointed as near the lump as I could, and fired away. But the bear didn't come he only clomb up higher, and got out on a limb, which helped me to see him better. I now loaded up again and fired, but this time he didn't move at all. I commenced loading for a third fire, but the first thing I knowed, the bear was down among my dogs, and they were fighting all around me.

I had my big butcher in my belt, and I had a pair of dressed buckskin breeches on. So I took out my knife, and stood, determined, if he should get hold of me, to defend myself in the best way I could. I stood there for some time, and could now and then see a white dog I had, but the rest of them, and the bear, which were dark-colored, I couldn't see at all, it was so miserable dark. They still fought around me, and sometimes within three feet of me; but, at last, the bear got down into one of the cracks, that the earthquakes had made in the ground, about four feet deep, and I could tell the biting end of him by the hollering of my dogs. So I took my gun and pushed the muzzle of it about, till I thought I had it against the main part of his body, and fired; but it happened to be only the fleshy part of his foreleg. With this, he jumped out of the crack, and he and the dogs had another hard fight around me, as before. At last, however, they forced him back into the crack again, as he was when I had shot.

I had laid down my gun in the dark, and I now began to hunt for it; and, while hunting, I got hold of a pole, and I concluded I would punch him awhile with that. I did so, and when I would punch him, the dogs would jump in on him, when he would bite them badly, and they would jump out again. I concluded, as he would take punching so patiently, it might be that he would lie still enough for me to get down in the crack, and feel slowly along till I could find the right place to give him a dig with my butcher. So I got down, and my dogs got in before him and kept his head towards them, till I got along easily up to him; and placing my hand on his rump, felt for his shoulder, just behind which I intended to stick him. I made a lounge with my long knife, and fortunately stuck him right through the heart; at which he just sank down, and I crawled out in a hurry. In a little time my dogs all come out too, and seemed satisfied, which was the way they always had of telling me that they had finished him.

I suffered very much that night with cold, as my leather breeches, and everything else I had on, was wet and frozen. But I managed to get my bear out of this crack after several hard trials, and so I butchered him, and laid down to try to sleep. But my fire was very bad, and I couldn't find anything that would burn well to make it any better; and I concluded I should freeze, if I didn't warm myself in some way by exercise. So I got up, and hollered awhile, and then I would just jump up and down with all my might, and throw myself into all sorts of motions. But all this wouldn't do; for my blood was now getting cold, and the chills coming all over me. I was so tired, too, that I could hardly walk; but I thought I would do the best I could to save my life, and then, if I died, nobody would be to blame. So I went to a tree about two feet through, and not a limb on it for thirty feet, and I would climb up it to the limbs, and then lock my arms together around it, and slide down to the bottom again. This would make the insides of my legs and arms feel mighty warm and good. I continued this till daylight in the morning, and how often I clomb up my tree and slid down I don't know, but I reckon at least a hundred times.

In the morning I got my bear hung up so as to be safe, and then set out to hunt for my camp. I found it after a while, and McDaniel and my son were very much rejoiced to see me get back, for they were about to give me up for lost. We got our breakfasts, and then secured our meat by building a high scaffold, and covering it over. We had no fear of its spoiling, for the weather was so cold that it couldn't.

Keeping Warm

We now started after my other bear, which had caused me so much trouble and suffering; and before we got him, we got a start after another, and took him also. We went on to the creek I had crossed the night before and camped, and then went to where my bear was, that I had killed in the crack. When we examined the place, McDaniel said he wouldn't have gone into it, as I did, for all the bears in the woods.

We took the meat down to our camp and salted it, and also the last one we had killed; intending, in the morning, to make a hunt in the harricane again.

We prepared for resting that night, and I can assure the reader I was in need of it. We had laid down by our fire, and about ten o'clock there came a most terrible earthquake, which shook the earth so, that we were rocked about like we had been in a cradle. We were very much alarmed; for though we were accustomed to feel earthquakes, we were now right in the region which had been torn to pieces by them in 1812, and we thought it might take a notion and swallow us up, like the big fish did Jonah.

In the morning we packed up and moved to the harricane, where we made another camp, and turned out that evening and killed a very large bear, which made *eight* we had now killed in this hunt.

The next morning we entered the harricane again, and in little or no time my dogs were in full cry. We pursued them, and soon came to a thick cane-brake, in which they had stop'd their bear. We got up close to him, as the cane was so thick that we couldn't see more than a few feet. Here I made my friend hold the cane a little open with his gun till I shot the bear, which was a mighty large one. I killed him dead in his tracks. We got him out and butch-

ered him, and in a little time started another and killed
him, which now made *ten* we had killed; and we know'd
we couldn't pack any more home, as we had only five
horses along; therefore we returned to the camp and salted
up all our meat, to be ready for a start homeward next
morning.

The morning came, and we packed our horses with the
meat, and had as much as they could possibly carry, and
sure enough cut out for home. It was about thirty miles,
and we reached home the second day. I had now accom-
modated my neighbor with meat enough to do him, and
had killed in all, up to that time, fifty-eight bears, during
the fall and winter.

As soon as the time come for them to quit their houses
and come out again in the spring, I took a notion to hunt
a little more, and in about one month I killed forty-seven
more, which made one hundred and five bears I had killed
in less than one year from that time.

A Useful Coonskin

From 'Oddities in Southern Life and Character,' ed. by Henry Watterson, 1882

CROCKETT the politician is, if possible, an even more engaging figure than Crockett the hunter. The suggestion that he run for Congress was first made to the Colonel as a joke. He decided to take it seriously, and his local popularity was such that he was elected for three terms, 1827–31, and 1833–35. His electioneering campaigns were enlivened with humor and horseplay in the best backwoods tradition — of which the yarn reprinted here is a characteristic sample.

In politics Colonel Crockett was in opposition to his old chief General Jackson. 'I let the people know ... that I wouldn't take a collar around my neck with the letters engraved on it, "MY DOG — Andrew Jackson."' A hero in anti-Jackson circles, he was fêted everywhere during his celebrated 'tour of the north' in the spring of 1834. But the power of the administration finally brought about his defeat by a small majority. He promptly put into effect his election promise to the people: 'If you re-elect me to Congress, I will serve you faithfully. If you don't, you may go to the devil, and I will go to Texas.' Aroused by the cause of Texan independence, he set out for the front. He arrived at the Alamo in February, 1836, and was killed in its heroic defense.

This anecdote of Crockett's first campaign for Congress is taken from *Oddities in Southern Life and Character*, edited by Henry Watterson (Boston and New York: Houghton Mifflin Company, 1882).

A Useful Coonskin

WHILE on the subject of election matters, I will just relate a little anecdote about myself, which will show the people to the east how we manage these things on the frontiers. It was when I first ran for Congress; I was then in favor of the Hero, for he had chalked out his course so sleek in his letter to the Tennessee Legislature that, like Sam Patch, says I, 'There can be no mistake in him,' and so I went ahead. No one dreamt about the Monster and the deposits at that time, and so, as I afterward found, many like myself were taken in by these fair promises, which were worth about as much as a flash in the pan when you have a fair shot at a fat bear.

But I am losing sight of my story. Well, I started off to the Cross Roads dressed in my hunting-shirt, and my rifle on my shoulder. Many of our constituents had assembled there to get a taste of the quality of the candidates at orating. Job Snelling, a gander-shanked Yankee, who had been caught somewhere about Plymouth Bay, and been shipped to the West with a cargo of codfish and rum, erected a large shanty, and set up shop for the occasion. A large posse of the voters had assembled before I arrived and my opponent had already made considerable headway with his speechifying and his treating, when they spied me about a rifle-shot from the camp, sauntering along as if I was not a party in business. 'There comes Crockett,' cried one. 'Let us hear the colonel,' cried another; and so I mounted the stump that had been cut down for the occasion, and began to bushwhack in the most approved style.

I had not been up long before there was such an uproar in the crowd that I could not hear my own voice, and some of my constituents let me know that they could not listen to me on such a dry subject as the welfare of the nation until they had something to drink, and that I must treat them. Accordingly I jumped down from the rostrum, and led the way to the shanty, followed by my constituents, shouting, 'Huzza for Crockett!' and 'Crockett forever!'

When we entered the shanty Job was busy dealing out his rum in a style that showed he was making a good day's work of it, and I called for a quart of the best; but the crooked crittur returned no other answer than by pointing to a board over the bar, on which he had chalked in large letters, 'Pay today and trust tomorrow.' Now that idea brought me up all standing; it was a sort of cornering in which there was no back-out, for ready money in the West, in those times, was the shyest thing in all natur, and it was most particularly shy with me on that occasion.

The voters, seeing my predicament, fell off to the other side, and I was left deserted and alone, as the Government will be, when he no longer has any offices to bestow. I saw as plain as day that the tide of popular opinion was against me, and that unless I got some rum speedily I should lose my election as sure as there are snakes in Virginny; and it must be done soon, or even burnt brandy wouldn't save me. So I walked away from the shanty, but in another guess sort from the way I entered it, for on this occasion I had no train after me, and not a voice shouted, 'Huzza for

Crockett!' Popularity sometimes depends on a very small matter, indeed; in this particular it was worth a quart of New England rum, and no more.

Well, knowing that a crisis was at hand, I struck into the woods, with my rifle on my shoulder, my best friend in time of need; and, as good fortune would have it, I had not been out more than a quarter of an hour before I treed a fat coon, and in the pulling of a trigger he lay dead at the root of the tree. I soon whipped his hairy jacket off his back, and again bent my steps toward the shanty, and walked up to the bar, but not alone, for this time I had half a dozen of my constituents at my heels. I threw down the coonskin upon the counter, and called for a quart, and Job, though busy in dealing out rum, forgot to point at his chalked rules and regulations; for he knew that a coon was as good a legal tender for a quart in the West as a New York shilling any day in the year.

My constituents now flocked about me, and cried, 'Huzza for Crockett!' 'Crockett forever!' and finding the tide had taken a turn, I told them several yarns, to get them in a good humor; and having soon dispatched the value of the coon, I went out and mounted the stump without opposition, and a clear majority of the voters followed me to hear what I had to offer for the good of the nation. Before I was half through, one of my constituents moved that they would hear the balance of my speech after they had washed down the first part with some more of Job Snelling's extract of cornstalk and molasses, and the question being put, it was carried unanimously. It wasn't considered necessary to tell the yeas and nays, so we adjourned to the shanty, and on the way I began to reckon that the fate of the nation pretty much depended upon my shooting another coon.

While standing at the bar, feeling sort of bashful while Job's rules and regulations stared me in the face, I cast down my eyes and discovered one end of the coonskin sticking between the logs that supported the bar. Job had slung it there in the hurry of business. I gave it a sort of quick jerk, and it followed my hand as natural as if I had been the rightful owner. I slapped it on the counter, and Job, little dreaming that he was barking up the wrong tree, shoved along another bottle, which my constituents quickly disposed of with great good humor, for some of them saw the trick; and then we withdrew to the rostrum to discuss the affairs of the nation.

I don't know how it was, but the voters soon became

Legal Tender for a Quart

dry again, and nothing would do but we must adjourn to the shanty; and as luck would have it, the coonskin was still sticking between the logs, as if Job had flung it there on purpose to tempt me. I was not slow in raising it to the counter, the rum followed, of course, and I wish I may be shot if I didn't, before the day was over, get ten quarts for the same identical skin, and from a fellow, too, who in those parts was considered as sharp as a steel trap and as bright as a pewter button.

This joke secured me my election, for it soon circulated like smoke among my constituents, and they allowed, with one accord, that the man who could get the whip hand of Job Snelling in fair trade could outwit Old Nick himself, and was the real grit for them in Congress. Job was by no means popular; he boasted of always being wide awake, and that anyone who could take him in was free to do so, for he came from a stock that, sleeping or waking, had always one eye open, and the other not more than half closed. The whole family were geniuses. His father was the inventor of wooden nutmegs, by which Job said he might have made a fortune, if he had only taken out a patent and kept the business in his own hands; his mother, Patience, manufactured the first white-oak pumpkin seeds of the mammoth kind, and turned a pretty penny the first season; and his aunt Prudence was the first to discover that corn husks, steeped in tobacco water, would make as handsome Spanish wrappers as ever came from Havana, and that oak leaves would answer all the purpose of filling, for no one could discover the difference except the man who smoked them, and then it would be too late to make a stir about it. Job himself bragged of having made some useful discoveries, the most profitable of which was the art of converting mahogany sawdust into cayenne pepper, which he said was a profitable and safe business; for the people have been so long accustomed to having dust thrown in their eyes that there wasn't much danger of being found out.

The way I got to the blind side of the Yankee merchant was pretty generally known before election day, and the result was that my opponent might as well have whistled jigs to a milestone as attempt to beat up for votes in that district. I beat him out and out, quite back into the old year, and there was scarce enough left of him, after the canvass was over, to make a small grease spot. He disappeared without even leaving a mark behind; and such will be the fate of Adam Huntsman, if there is a fair fight and no gouging.

After the election was over, I sent Snelling the price of the rum, but took good care to keep the fact from the knowledge of my constituents. Job refused the money, and sent me word that it did him good to be taken in occasionally, as it served to brighten his ideas; but I afterward learnt when he found out the trick that had been played upon him, he put all the rum I had ordered in his bill against my opponent, who, being elated with the speeches he had made on the affairs of the nation, could not descend to examine into the particulars of a bill of a vender of rum in the small way.

Jim Beckwourth

Chief of the Crows

From Beckwourth's 'Life and Adventures,' written from his own dictation by T. D. Bonner, 1856

AS THE Frontier flows westward beyond the Mississippi, the high-pitched appellations of the backwoods giants — Salt River Roarer, Sea-Horse of the Mountain, Game Cock of the Wilderness — seem almost pale beside the simple term 'mountain man.' To this grand company, Jim Beckwourth belongs. Though in 1855 he was 'personally known to thousands of people "living on both sides of the mountains,"' he never achieved heroic stature in popular history. His claim to fame rests on his unique autobiography, which Bernard DeVoto terms 'the best social history of the old West.'

Beckwourth (or Beckwith) was born in Virginia in 1798, of a mulatto mother and a white father. At twenty-five he joined General Ashley's great fur brigade, exploring the mountain territory in the Far Northwest. He was with Ashley on the amazing winter expedition of 1824-25, to the Platte and Green River country, and he stayed on under Ashley's successors until the fall of 1826, when he went to live among the Crows. One of the choicest bits in the autobiography is the account of Jim's adoption by the Crow Nation. As he explains in a previous passage, the savages were already prepared, through the joke of a squaw-man named Greenwood, to receive him as a long-lost son. It was a convenient arrangement for Beckwourth, who could hunt and trap unmolested from Indian attack in the heart of the fur country. For six years he remained with the Crows, outdoing them in their own savage way of life. 'After ten thousand adventures,' writes Bonner, '[he] finally became involved in the stream that set toward the Pacific, and, almost unconsciously, he established a home in one of the pleasant valleys that border on Feather River.' (In the Sierra Nevadas, north of Sacramento.) It was here that Bonner met him. In later years he lived in Denver; but when he died in 1867 he was back in Absaroka, among his old friends, the Crows.

The Life and Adventures of James P. Beckwourth, Mountaineer, Scout, and Pioneer, and Chief of the Crow Nation of Indians, written from his own dictation, by T. D. Bonner (New York: Harper & Brothers, 1856), has been reprinted with an excellent Introduction by Bernard DeVoto in the *Americana Deserta Series* (Knopf, 1931). The text here is from Chapter XII of the first edition.

Jim Beckwourth

I NOW parted with very many of my friends for the last time. Most of the members of that large company now sleep in death, their waking ears no longer to be filled with the death-telling yell of the savage. The manly hearts that shrunk from no danger have ceased to beat; their bones whiten in the gloomy fastnesses of the Rocky Mountains, or moulder on the ever-flowering prairies of the far West. A cloven skull is all that remains of my once gallant friends to tell the bloody death that they died, and invoke vengeance on the merciless hand that struck them down in their ruddy youth.

Here I parted from the boy Baptiste, who had been my faithful companion so long. I never saw him again.

The party that I started with consisted of thirty-one men, most of them skillful trappers (Captain Bridger was in our party), and commanded by Robert Campbell. We started for Powder River, a fork of the Yellow Stone, and, arriving there without accident, were soon busied in our occupation.

A circumstance occurred in our encampment on this stream, trivial in itself (for trivial events sometimes determine the course of a man's life), but which led to unexpected results. I had set my six traps overnight, and on

going to them the following morning I found four beavers,
but one of my traps was missing. I sought it in every
direction, but without success, and on my return to camp
mentioned the mystery. Captain Bridger (as skillful a
hunter as ever lived in the mountains) offered to renew
the search with me, expressing confidence that the trap
could be found. We searched diligently along the river and
the bank for a considerable distance, but the trap was
among the missing. The float-pole also was gone — a pole
ten or twelve feet long and four inches thick. We at
length gave it up as lost.

The next morning the whole party moved farther up the
river. To shorten our route, Bridger and myself crossed
the stream at the spot where I had set my missing trap.
It was a buffalo-crossing, and there was a good trail worn
in the banks, so that we could easily cross with our horses.
After passing and traveling on some two miles, I discovered what I supposed to be a badger, and we both made a
rush for him. On closer inspection, however, it proved to
be my beaver, with trap, chain, and float-pole. It was ap-
parent that some buffalo, in crossing the river, had become
entangled in the chain, and, as we conceived, had carried
the trap on his shoulder, with the beaver pendent on one
side and the pole on the other. We inferred that he had in
some way got his head under the chain, between the trap
and the pole, and, in his endeavors to extricate himself,
had pushed his head through. The hump on his back
would prevent it passing over his body, and away he
would speed with his burden, probably urged forward by
the four sharp teeth of the beaver, which would doubtless
object to his sudden equestrian (or rather bovine) journey.
We killed the beaver and took his skin, feeling much

satisfaction at the solution of the mystery. When we arrived at camp, we asked our companions to guess how and where we had found the trap. They all gave various guesses, but, failing to hit the truth, gave up the attempt.

'Well, gentlemen,' said I, 'it was stolen.'

'Stolen!' exclaimed a dozen voices at once.

'Yes, it was stolen by a buffalo.'

'Oh, come, now,' said one of the party, 'what is the use of coming here and telling such a lie?'

I saw in a moment that he was angry and in earnest, and I replied, 'If you deny that a buffalo stole my trap, *you* tell the lie.'

He rose and struck me a blow with his fist. It was my turn now, and the first pass I made brought my antagonist to the ground. On rising, he sprang for his gun; I assumed mine as quickly. The bystanders rushed between us, and, seizing our weapons, compelled us to discontinue our strife, which would have infallibly resulted in the death of one. My opponent mounted his horse and left the camp. I never saw him afterward. I could have taken his expression in jest, for we were very free in our sallies upon one another; but in this particular instance I saw his intention was to insult me, and I allowed my passion to overcome my reflection. My companions counseled me to leave camp for a few days until the ill feeling should have subsided.

The same evening Captain Bridger and myself started out with our traps, intending to be gone three or four days. We followed up a small stream until it forked, when Bridger proposed that I should take one fork and he the other, and the one who had set his traps first should cross the hill which separated the two streams and rejoin the other. Thus we parted, expecting to meet again in a few hours. I continued my course up the stream in pursuit of beaver villages until I found myself among an innumerable drove of horses, and I could plainly see they were not wild ones.

The horses were guarded by several of their Indian owners, or horse-guards, as they term them, who had discovered me long before I saw them. I could hear their signals to each other, and in a few moments I was surrounded by them, and escape was impossible. I resigned myself to my fate: if they were enemies, I knew they could kill me but once, and to attempt to defend myself would entail inevitable death. I took the chances between death and mercy; I surrendered my gun, traps, and what else I had, and was marched to camp under a strong escort of horse-guards. I felt very sure that my guards were Crows; therefore I did not feel greatly alarmed at my situation. On arriving at their village, I was ushered into the chief's lodge, where there were several old men and women, whom I conceived to be members of the family.

Defiance

My capture was known throughout the village in five minutes, and hundreds gathered around the lodge to get a sight of the prisoner. In the crowd were some who had talked to Greenwood a few weeks before. They at once exclaimed, 'That is the lost Crow, the great brave who has killed so many of our enemies. He is our brother.'

This threw the whole village into commotion; old and young were impatient to obtain a sight of the 'great brave.' Orders were immediately given to summon all the old women taken by the Shi-ans at the time of their captivity so many winters past, who had suffered the loss of a son at that time. The lodge was cleared for the *examining committee*, and the old women, breathless with excitement, their eyes wild and protruding and their nostrils dilated, arrived in squads, until the lodge was filled to overflowing. I believe never was mortal gazed at with such intense and sustained interest as I was on that occasion. Arms and legs were critically scrutinized. My face next passed the ordeal; then my neck, back, breast, and all parts of my body, even down to my feet, which did not escape the examination of these anxious matrons, in their endeavors to discover some mark or peculiarity whereby to recognize their brave son.

At length one old woman, after having scanned my visage with the utmost intentness, came forward and said, 'If this is my son, he has a mole over one of his eyes.'

My eyelids were immediately pulled down to the utmost stretch of their elasticity, when, sure enough, she discovered a mole just over my left eye!

'Then, and oh then!' such shouts of joy as were uttered by that honest-hearted woman were seldom before heard, while all in the crowd took part in her rejoicing. It was uncultivated joy, but not the less heartfelt and intense. It was a joy which a mother can only experience when she recovers a son whom she had supposed dead in his earliest days. She has mourned him silently through weary nights and busy days for the long space of twenty years; suddenly he presents himself before her in robust manhood, and graced with the highest name an Indian can appreciate. It is but nature, either in the savage breast or civilized, that hails such a return with overwhelming joy, and feels the mother's undying affection awakened beyond all control.

All the other claimants resigning their pretensions, I was fairly carried along by the excited crowd to the lodge of the 'Big Bowl,' who was my father. The news of my having proved to be the son of Mrs. Big Bowl flew through the village with the speed of lightning, and, on my arrival at the paternal lodge, I found it filled with all degrees of my newly discovered relatives, who welcomed me nearly to death. They seized me in their arms and hugged me, and my face positively burned with the enraptured kisses of my numerous fair sisters, with a long host of cousins, aunts, and other more remote kindred. All these welcoming ladies as firmly believed in my identity with the lost one as they believed in the existence of the Great Spirit.

My father knew me to be his son; told all the Crows that the dead was alive again, and the lost one was found. He knew it was fact; Greenwood had said so, and the words of Greenwood were true; his tongue was not crooked — he would not lie. He also had told him that his son was a great brave among the white men; that his arm was strong; that the Black Feet quailed before his rifle and battle-axe; that his lodge was full of their scalps which his knife had taken; that they must rally around me to support and protect me; and that his long-lost son would be a strong breastwork to their nation, and he would teach them how to defeat their enemies.

They all promised that they would do as his words had indicated.

My unmarried sisters were four in number, very pretty, intelligent young women. They, as soon as the departure of the crowd would admit, took off my old leggins, and moccasins, and other garments, and supplied their place with new ones, most beautifully ornamented according to their very last fashion. My sisters were very ingenious in such work, and they well-nigh quarreled among themselves for the privilege of dressing me. When my toilet was finished to their satisfaction, I could compare in elegance with the most popular warrior of the tribe when in full costume. They also prepared me a bed, not so high as Haman's gallows certainly, but just as high as the lodge would admit. This was also a token of their esteem and sisterly affection.

While conversing to the extent of my ability with my father in the evening, and affording him full information respecting the white people, their great cities, their numbers, their power, their opulence, he suddenly demanded if I wanted a wife; thinking, no doubt, that, if he got me married, I should lose all discontent, and forego any wish of returning to the whites.

I assented, of course.

'Very well,' said he, 'you shall have a pretty wife and a good one.'

Away he strode to the lodge of one of the greatest braves, and asked one of his daughters of him to bestow

Jim Beckwourth, Chief of the Crows

upon his son, who the chief must have heard was also a great brave. The consent of the parent was readily given. The name of my prospective father-in-law was Black-lodge. He had three very pretty daughters, whose names were Still-water, Black-fish, and Three-roads.

Even the untutored daughters of the wild woods need a little time to prepare for such an important event, but long and tedious courtships are unknown among them.

The ensuing day the three daughters were brought to my father's lodge by their father, and I was requested to take my choice. 'Still-water' was the eldest and I liked her name; if it was emblematic of her disposition, she was the woman I should prefer. 'Still-water,' accordingly, was my choice. They were all superbly attired in garments which must have cost them months of labor, which garments the young women ever keep in readiness against such an interesting occasion as the present.

The acceptance of my wife was the completion of the ceremony, and I was again a married man, as sacredly in their eyes as if the Holy Christian Church had fastened the irrevocable knot upon us.

Among the Indians the daughter receives no patrimony on her wedding-day, and her mother and father never pass a word with the son-in-law after — a custom religiously observed among them, though for what reason I never learned. The other relatives are under no such restraint.

My brothers made me a present of twenty as fine horses as any in the nation — all trained war-horses. I was also presented with all the arms and instruments requisite for an Indian campaign.

My wife's deportment coincided with her name; she

would have reflected honor upon many a civilized household. She was affectionate, obedient, gentle, cheerful, and, apparently, quite happy. No domestic thunder storms, no curtain-lectures, ever disturbed the serenity of our connubial lodge. I speedily formed acquaintance with all my immediate neighbors, and the Morning Star (which was the name conferred upon me on my recognition as the lost son) was soon a companion to all the young warriors in the village. No power on earth could have shaken their faith in my positive identity with the lost son. Nature seemed to prompt the old woman to recognize me as her missing child, and all my new relatives placed implicit faith in the genuineness of her discovery. Greenwood had spoken it, 'and his tongue was not crooked.' What could I do under the circumstances? Even if I should deny my Crow origin, they would not believe me. How could I dash with an unwelcome and incredible explanation all the joy that had been manifested on my return — the cordial welcome, the rapturous embraces of those who hailed me as a son and a brother, the exuberant joy of the whole nation for the return of a long-lost Crow, who, stolen when a child, had returned in the strength of maturity, graced with the name of a great brave, and the generous strife I had occasioned in their endeavors to accord me the warmest welcome? I could not find it in my heart to undeceive these unsuspecting people and tear myself away from their untutored caresses.

Thus I commenced my Indian life with the Crows. I said to myself, 'I can trap in their streams unmolested, and derive more profit under their protection than if among my own men, exposed incessantly to assassination and alarm.' I therefore resolved to abide with them, to guard my secret, to do my best in their company, and in assisting them to subdue their enemies.

There was but one recollection troubled me, and that was my lonely one in St. Louis. My thoughts were constantly filled with her. I knew my affection was recip-rocated, and that her fond heart beat alone for me; that my promise was undoubtingly confided in, and that prayers were daily offered for my safety, thus distant in the mountains, exposed to every peril. Repeatedly I would appoint a day for my return, but some unexpected event would occur and thrust my resolution aside. Still I hoped, for I had accumulated the means of wealth suffi-cient to render us comfortable through life; a fortunate re-turn was all I awaited to consummate my ardent anticipa-tion of happiness, and render me the most blessed of mortals.

Before proceeding farther with my Indian life, I will conduct the reader back to our camp the evening succeed-ing my disappearance from Bridger. He was on the hill, crossing over to me as agreed upon, when he saw me in the hands of the Indians, being conducted to their village, which was also in sight. Seeing clearly that he could op-pose no resistance to my captors, he made all speed to the camp, and communicated the painful news of my death. He had seen me in the charge of a whole host of Shi-ans, who were conducting me to camp, there to sacrifice me in the most approved manner their savage propensities could suggest, and then abandon themselves to a general rejoicing over the fall of a white man. With the few men he had in camp it was hopeless to attempt a rescue; for, judging by the size of the village, there must be a commun-ity of several thousand Indians. All were plunged in

At Peace with the Mountain Men

gloom. All pronounced my funeral eulogy; all my daring encounters were spoken of to my praise. My fortunate escapes, my repeated victories were applauded in memory of me; the loss of their best hunter, of their kind and ever-obliging friend, was deeply deplored by all.

'Alas! had it not been for that lamentable quarrel,' they exclaimed, 'he would still have been among us. Poor Jim! Peace to his ashes!'

Bridger lamented that he had advised me to leave the camp, and again that he had separated from me at the Forks. 'If we had kept together,' he murmured, 'his fate might have been prevented, for doubtless one of us would have seen the Indians in time to have escaped.'

Thus, as I was afterward informed by some of the party, was my memory celebrated in that forlorn camp. Further, having conceived a deep disgust at that vicinity, they moved their camp to the headwaters of the Yellow Stone, leaving scores of beavers unmolested in the streams.

The faithful fellows little thought that, while they were lamenting my untimely fall, I was being hugged and kissed to death by a whole lodge full of near and dear Crow relatives, and that I was being welcomed with a public reception fully equal in intensity, though not in extravagance, to that accorded to the victor of Waterloo on his triumphal entry into Paris.

Bridger had never supposed that the Indians whom he saw leading me away were Crows, he being ignorant that he was so near their territory. His impression was that these were Cheyennes, hence I was given up for dead and reported so to others. My death was communicated to the rendezvous when the fall hunt was over, and there was a general time of mourning in mountain style.

I say 'mountain style' in contradistinction to the manner of civilized circles, because, with them, when the death of a comrade is deplored, his good deeds alone are celebrated; his evil ones are interred with his bones. Modern politics have introduced the custom of perpetuating all that is derogatory to a man's fair fame, and burying in deep oblivion all that was honorable and praiseworthy. Hence I say, Give me the mountaineer, despite all the opprobrium that is cast upon his name, for in him you have a man of chivalrous feeling, ready to divide his last morsel with his distressed fellow — ay, and to yield the last drop of his blood to defend the life of his friend.

The Big Bear of Arkansas

By T. B. Thorpe, *1841*

IF THERE is one tall tale most typical of the genus, it is probably 'The Big Bear of Arkansas.' 'It was in fact a creation bar,' as the man of Arkansaw said; and that in more senses than one. In its wake came scores of similar yarns. They are closely related both to earlier printed stories about Fink, Crockett, *et al.*, and to the fantastic whoppers still current in remote regions — like the Paul Bunyan legends in the North Woods or the tall tales that Percy MacKaye found in the Kentucky Mountains.

'The Big Bear of Arkansas' first appeared in William T. Porter's *Spirit of the Times* in 1841. It was the title story of a collection edited by Porter in 1845, from a later edition of which the text here is taken (Philadelphia, 1858). It also appears in Thorpe's *The Hive of the Bee-Hunter* (1854). It has been reprinted in Franklin J. Meine's *Tall Tales of the Southwest* (1930).

Only the story of the bear hunt itself is given here, space unfortunately not permitting the inclusion of the delightful introductory pages. The scene is the 'high-pressure-and-beat-every-thing' steamboat *Invincible*. The tale is told by a famous hunter, himself known as 'The Big Bear of Arkansas,' to a receptive traveler from New Orleans.

The Big Bear of Arkansas

S TRANGER,' said he, 'in bar hunts I am numerous, and which particular one, as you say, I shall tell, puzzles me. There was the old she devil I shot at the Hurricane last fall — then there was the old hog thief I popped over at the Bloody Crossing, and then —— Yes, I have it! I will give you an idea of a hunt, in which the greatest bar was killed that ever lived, none excepted; about an old fellow that I hunted, more or less, for two or three years; and if that ain't a particular bar hunt, I ain't got one to tell. But in the first place, stranger, let me say, I am pleased with you, because you ain't ashamed to gain information by asking, and listening, and that's what I say to Countess's pups every day when I'm home; and I have got great hopes of them ar pups, because they are continually nosing about; and though they stick it some-times in the wrong place, they gain experience anyhow, and may learn something useful to boot. Well, as I was saying about this big bar, you see, when I and some more first settled in our region, we were driven to hunting naturally; we soon liked it, and after that we found it an easy matter to make the thing our business. One old chap who had pioneered afore us, gave us to understand that we had settled in the right place. He dwelt upon its merits

until it was affecting, and showed us, to prove his asser-
tions, more marks on the sassafras trees than I ever saw
on a tavern door 'lection time. "Who keeps that ar reckon-
ing?" said I. "The bar," said he. "What for?" said I.
"Can't tell," said he; "but so it is: the bar bite the bark

and wood too, at the highest point from the ground they
can reach, and you can tell, by the marks," said he, "the
length of the bar to an inch." "Enough," said I; "I've
learned something here a' ready, and I'll put it in practice."
    'Well, stranger, just one month from that time I killed
a bar, and told its exact length before I measured it, by
those very marks; and when I did that, I swelled up con-

siderable — I've been a prouder man ever since. So I went on, larning something every day, until I was reckoned a buster, and allowed to be decidedly the best bar hunter in my district; and that is a reputation as much harder to earn than to be reckoned first man in Congress as an iron ramrod is harder than a toadstool. Did the varmints grow overcunning by being fooled with by greenhorn hunters, and by this means get troublesome, they send for me as a matter of course; and thus I do my own hunting, and most of my neighbors'. I walk into the varmints, though, and it has become about as much the same to me as drinking. It is told in two sentences — a bar is started, and he is killed. The thing is somewhat monotonous now — I know just how much they will run, where they will tire, how much they will growl, and what a thundering time I will have in getting them home. I could give you this history of the chase with all particulars at the commencement, I know the signs so well — stranger, I'm certain. Once I met with a match, though, and I will tell you about it; for a common hunt would not be worth relating.

'On a fine fall day, long time ago, I was trailing about for bar, and what should I see but fresh marks on the sassafras trees, about eight inches above any in the forests that I knew of. Says I, "Them marks is a hoax, or it indicates the d——t bar that was ever grown." In fact, stranger, I couldn't believe it was real, and I went on. Again I saw the same marks, at the same height, and I knew the thing lived. That conviction came home to my soul like an earthquake. Says I, "Here is something a-purpose for me: that bar is mine, or I give up the hunting business." The very next morning what should I see but a number of buzzards hovering over my cornfield. "The rascal has been there," said I, "for that sign is certain": and, sure enough, on examining, I found the bones of what had been as beautiful a hog the day before as was ever raised by a Buckeye. Then I tracked the critter out of the field to the woods, and all the marks he left behind showed me that he was the bar.

'Well, stranger, the first fair chase I ever had with that big critter, I saw him no less than three distinct times at a distance: the dogs run him over eighteen miles and broke down, my horse gave out, and I was as nearly used up as a man can be, made on my principle, which is patent. Before this adventure, such things were unknown to me as possible; but, strange as it was, that bar got me used to it before I was done with him; for he got so at last that he would leave me on a long chase quite easy. How he did it, I never could understand. That a bar runs at all is puzzling; but how this one could tire down and bust up a pack of hounds and a horse, that were used to overhauling everything they started after in no time, was past my understanding. Well, stranger, that bar finally got so sassy that he used to help himself to a hog off my premises whenever he wanted one; the buzzards followed after what he left, and so between bar and buzzard, I rather think I was out of pork.

'Well, missing that bar so often took hold of my vitals, and I wasted away. The thing had been carried too far, and it reduced me in flesh faster than an ager. I would see that bar in everything I did: he hunted me, and that, too, like a devil, which I began to think he was. While in this fix, I made preparations to give him a last brush, and be done with it. Having completed everything to my satisfaction, I started at sunrise, and to my great joy, I discovered from the way the dogs run that they were near him; finding his trail was nothing, for that had become as plain to the pack as a turnpike road. On he went, and coming to an open country, what should I see but the bar very leisurely ascending a hill, and the dogs close at his heels, either a match for him in speed, or else he did not care to get out of their way — I don't know which. But wasn't he a beauty, though? I loved him like a brother.

'On he went, until he came to a tree, the limbs of which formed a crotch about six feet from the ground. Into this crotch he got and seated himself, the dogs yelling all around it; and there he sat eyeing them as quiet as a pond in low water. A greenhorn friend of mine, in company, reached shooting distance before me, and blazed away, hitting the critter in the center of his forehead. The bar shook his head as the ball struck it, and then walked down from that tree as gently as a lady would from a carriage.

'Twas a beautiful sight to see him do that — he was in
such a rage that he seemed to be as little afraid of the dogs
as if they had been sucking pigs; and the dogs warn't slow
in making a ring around him a respectful distance, I tell
you; even Bowie Knife, himself, stood off. Then the way

his eyes flashed — why, the fire of them would have singed
a cat's hair; in fact that bar was a wrath all over. Only
one pup came near him, and he was brushed out so totally
with the bar's left paw that he entirely disappeared; and
that made the old dogs more cautious still.

'In the meantime, I came up, and taking deliberate aim
as a man should do, at his side, just back of his foreleg, if
my gun did not snap, call me a coward, and I won't take it
personal. Yes, stranger, it snapped, and I could not find a
cap about my person. While in this predicament, I
turned round to my fool friend — says I, "Bill," says I,
"you're an ass — you're a fool — you might as well have
tried to kill that bar by barking the tree under his belly,
as to have done it by hitting him in the head. Your shot

has made a tiger of him, and blast me, if a dog gets killed or wounded when they come to blows, I will stick my knife into your liver, I will" — my wrath was up. I had lost my caps, my gun had snapped, the fellow with me had fired at the bar's head, and I expected every moment to see him close in with the dogs and kill a dozen of them at least.

'In this thing I was mistaken, for the bar leaped over the ring formed by the dogs, and, giving a fierce growl, was off — the pack, of course, in full cry after him. The run this time was short, for coming to the edge of a lake the varmint jumped in, and swam to a little island in the lake, which it reached just a moment before the dogs. "I'll have him now," said I — for I had found my caps in the lining of my coat — so, rolling a log into the lake, I paddled myself across to the island, just as the dogs had cornered the bar in a thicket. I rushed up and fired — at the same time the critter leaped over the dogs and came within three feet of me, running like mad; he jumped into the lake, and tried to mount the log I had just deserted, but every time he got half his body on it, it would roll over and send him under; the dogs, too, got around him, and pulled him about, and finally Bowie Knife clinched with him, and they sunk into the lake together. Stranger, about this time, I was excited, and I stripped off my coat, drew my knife, and intended to have taken a part with Bowie Knife myself, when the bar rose to the surface. But the varmint stayed under — Bowie Knife came up alone, more dead than alive, and with the pack came ashore. "Thank God," said I, "the old villain has got his deserts at last."

'Determined to have the body, I cut a grapevine for a

rope, and dove down where I could see the bar in the
water, fastened my queer rope to his leg, and fished him,
with great difficulty, ashore. Stranger, may I be chawed
to death by young alligators if the thing I looked at
wasn't a she bar, and not the old critter after all. The way
matters got mixed on that island was onaccountably
curious, and thinking of it made me more than ever con-
vinced that I was hunting the devil himself.

'I went home that night and took to my bed — the
thing was killing me. The entire team of Arkansaw in bar-
hunting acknowledged himself used up, and the fact sunk
into my feelings like a snagged boat will in the Mississippi.
I grew as cross as a bar with two cubs and a sore tail. The
thing got out 'mong my neighbors, and I was asked how-
come on that individ-u-al that never lost a bar when once
started? and if that same individ-u-al didn't wear tele-
scopes when he turned a she bar, of ordinary size, into an
old he one, a little larger than a horse? "Perhaps," said I,
"friends" — getting wrathy — "perhaps you want to call
somebody a liar." "Oh, no," said they, "we only heard
such things as being rather common of late, but we don't
believe one word of it; oh, no" — and then they would ride
off and laugh like so many hyenas over a dead nigger.

'It was too much, and I determined to catch that bar, go
to Texas, or die — and I made my preparations accordin'.
I had the pack shut up and rested. I took my rifle to
pieces and iled it. I put caps in every pocket about my
person, for fear of the lining. I then told my neighbors
that on Monday morning — naming the day — I would
start THAT BAR, and bring him home with me, or they
might divide my settlement among them, the owner having disappeared.

'*A Creation Bar*'

'Well, stranger, on the morning previous to the great day of my hunting expedition, I went into the woods near my house, taking my gun and Bowie Knife along, just from habit, and there, sitting down also from habit, what should I see, getting over my fence, but the bar! Yes, the old varmint was within a hundred yards of me, and the way he walked over that fence — stranger, he loomed up like a black mist, he seemed so large, and he walked right toward me. I raised myself, took deliberate aim, and fired. Instantly the varmint wheeled, gave a yell, and walked through the fence like a falling tree would through a cobweb. I started after, but was tripped up by my in-expressibles, which either from habit, or the excitement of the moment, were about my heels, and before I had really gathered myself up, I heard the old varmint groaning in a thicket near-by, like a thousand sinners, and by the time I reached him he was a corpse.

'Stranger, it took five niggers and myself to put that carcass on a mule's back, and old long-ears waddled under the load as if he was foundered in every leg of his body, and with a common whopper of a bar he would have trotted off, and enjoyed himself. 'Twould astonish you to know how big he was: I made a bedspread of his skin, and the way it used to cover my bar mattress, and leave several feet on each side to tuck up, would have delighted you. It was in fact a creation bar, and if it had lived in Samson's time, and had met him, in a fair fight, it would have licked him in the twinkling of a dice-box. But, stranger, I never like the way I hunted, and missed him. There is something curious about it, I could never under-stand — and I never was satisfied at his giving in so easy at last. Perhaps he had heard of my preparations to hunt him the next day, so he jist come in, like Captain Scott's coon, to save his wind to grunt with in dying; but that ain't likely. My private opinion is, that that bar was an unhuntable bar, and died when his time come.'

When the story was ended, our hero sat some minutes with his auditors in a grave silence; I saw there was a mystery to him connected with the bear whose death he had just related, that had evidently made a strong impression on his mind. It was also evident that there was some superstitious awe connected with the affair — a feeling common with all 'children of the wood,' when they meet with anything out of their everyday experience. He was the first one, however, to break the silence, and jumping up, he asked all present to 'liquor' before going to bed — a thing which he did, with a number of companions, evidently to his heart's content.

Long before day, I was put ashore at my place of destination, and I can only follow with the reader, in imagination, our Arkansas friend, in his adventures at the 'Forks of Cypress' on the Mississippi.

Kit Carson, Trapper

By Stanley Vestal. From 'Kit Carson,
Happy Warrior of the Old West,' 1928

AS BOONE and Crockett, by accumulation of legends, became the traditional heroes of Kentucky and Tennessee, so Kit Carson, a quarter of a century later, blossomed over night into a living symbol of the frontier beyond the Mississippi. He was born in Kentucky in 1809, and was brought up in Missouri; but life began for Kit at seventeen when he ran away and joined a Santa Fe Expedition. The Southwest held him; before he was twenty-one, he was a full-fledged 'mountain man' — a clever trapper and an Indian fighter with three brass tacks in the stock of his new rifle. Henceforth Taos, as much as any single spot could be, was his home.

The selection which follows, from Stanley Vestal's biography, shows Kit in 1831 at an interesting point in his career. Here is Kit the expert mountain trapper — and Kit the plainsman in the making.

Some ten years later, Carson joined as guide the first expedition of Frémont, whose Report brought him nation-wide notice. Through the rest of his adventurous life, which included guiding further expeditions, brilliant service in the Mexican War, work as an Indian agent, and occasional farming, he remained the Hero of the Prairies. Unlike many of the now famous frontiersmen, he was already a legendary giant when he died in 1868.

George W. Brewerton, who crossed the Plains with him in 1848, has left us a personal sketch (*Harper's New Monthly,* 1853):

'The Kit Carson of my *imagination* was over six feet high — a sort of modern Hercules in his build — with an enormous beard, and a voice like a roused lion, whose talk was all of "stirring incidents by flood and field." The *real* Kit Carson I found to be a plain, simple, unostentatious man; rather below the medium height, with brown, curling hair, little or no beard, and a voice as soft and gentle as a woman's. In fact, the hero of a hundred desperate encounters, whose life had been mostly spent amid wildernesses, where the white man is almost unknown, was one of Dame Nature's gentlemen — a sort of article which she gets up occasionally, but nowhere in better style than among the backwoods of America.'

Kit Carson, Trapper

AUTUMN days came at last. Snow appeared on the mountains, and bright splashes of yellowing aspens spotted their sides. Kit and the others were restless, grease-hungry for fat cow and mountain doin's, half froze for the trail and the chance of a Pawnee topknot. Even the simple civilized fixin's of primitive Taos were too effete and fofurraw for the trappers. With what savage gusto they spat out their pronunciation of the French word — *fanfaron* — that synonym for everything frivolous, showy, effeminate, unessential, belonging to the despised settlements. Fofurraw! Everything this side the mountains was too damned fofurraw!

When Thomas Fitzpatrick, partner in the newly formed Rocky Mountain Fur Company, rode into Taos looking for recruits, the eager mountain men enrolled in his service *en masse*. Fitzpatrick stood behind Ewing Young's bar and laboriously entered the names and debits of his men as each one pushed forward in turn to claim his equipment. The little room was jammed with the candidates. Broken Hand (as old Tom was called because of an injury due to the explosion of his gun) had the respect of every man present. They were glad to have him as their partisan.

Kit was pushed forward in his turn, and stared at his new boss. Tall and muscular, with sanguine complexion showing through his tan and thick beard, Thomas of the Broken Hand looked at Kit with piercing eyes from under the brim of his old wool hat. Those melancholy and un-compromising eyes seemed to have but a poor opinion of the stocky, sandy-haired young 'un who looked 'most too small to set a trap. But Ewing Young said a word in Tom's ear, and the new partisan took the quill between his shattered fingers and made entries in his book. The men watched in fascinated silence. To Kit, those illegible marks were significant. Now at last he was to head into the Rocky Mountains, the trappers' paradise.

Broken Hand scratched awkwardly in the small black book, reading each entry aloud as he proceeded:

Kit Carson

Dr.

Sept. 1830	To .... 1 saddle mule.............	30 plews
	To .... 1 Spanish saddle...........	40 plews
	To .... 1 capote, Hudson's Bay.....	8 plews
	To .... Galena lead pigs...........	1 plew
	To .... 3 feet Twist tobacco.......	1 plew
	To .... 6 traps..................	24 plews
	Total................	104 plews

'Next,' said Broken Hand, and Kit pushed his way out to get his plunder together for the long ride north. It would not take long to pay off that debt, once he got among the fur. Had he not overheard Ewing Young's whisper to the partisan: 'Yon's a likely beaver kitten, Tom'?... A plew, or, as the French had it, *plus*, was trapper slang for a prime beaver skin. But long usage had made it an arbitrary symbol of value, the coin of the mountains. Kit saddled up that afternoon and rode out

Kit Carson

of Taos with a few others, having told the partisan of their intended movement up the trail. Kit was eager to be on his way.

Next day Broken Hand got the party together and started, after considerable cussin' and rasslin' with refractory mules. They rode east from Taos through the hills, then turned north toward the Arkansas River. Their way lay along Greenhorn Creek and the Rio San Carlos, and they forded the Arkansas near the mouth of Fountain Creek, where the city of Pueblo, Colorado, stands now. Following Fountain Creek northward through the barren hills, Broken Hand's party crossed the ridge, rode down into the valley of Cherry Creek, and so came at last to the Platte. Trapping its tributaries as they went, they steadily moved along, reached Sweetwater, Green River, and Jackson's Hole. Somewhere in the Rocky Mountains there should be a Carson's Hole. But there is none, for he was too constantly a wanderer to associate his name with any of those lovely sheltered valleys of the ranges, those 'holes' or winter retreats beloved by the early mountain men. After all, Taos was Kit's hole, and no park or valley of the mountains he loved so well will bear his name forever.

When winter came on and the streams froze and the beaver retired to his lodge to hibernate, the trappers went into winter quarters on Salmon River. There they built their arched framework of saplings, covered with skins, and open on one side to the blazing fire. There they constructed their scaffolds for curing meat, and rigged a rack of poles or antlers on which to hang their fresh meat and traps and clothing. There were placed the graining blocks and stretching frames used in dressing the skins and peltries. Inside the hut were stowed the saddle, the packs, the buffalo robes and blankets for the bed, possible sack, rifle, hatchet. In the bottoms the mules grazed on the good grass or, when the snow was deep, gnawed the bark from cottonwood boughs cut down by their owners. It was a satisfying life. Game was plenty, for the buffalo came in swarms from the freezing plains, and the men feasted on fat cow and prairie oysters.

Kit was well pleased with his fall hunt. He had done well, and was becoming a really expert trapper. Already he had paid his debt to Broken Hand, and had besides two full packs of skins, each weighing a hundred pounds, and containing eighty beaver plews each. He had picked up some otter, fox, and muskrat skins as well, and had a bear rug to add to his blankets at night when the fire burned low and the wolves howled from the windy hills. He was enjoying the prestige also which belonged to the man who was a genuine *hivernan* or winterer.

That winter, while the beaver tails boiled in the pot to delicious tenderness and the aroma of coffee blended with whiffs of strong tobacco from his old black clay, Kit and his comrades would hear Jim Bridger vie with the best in telling the whoppers beloved by the mountain men.

'Why, boys,' Jim would begin, solemnly, rolling his eyes and spitting deliberately into the embers, 'you know I fust come out with Ashley. Wagh! When I come west, yon hill was only a hole in the ground. Off-hand, or with a rest, I make 'em come. Thar ain't a varmint in the mountings thet I hain't et. I knows sign when I sees it.... But oncet I seen something thet made me feel almighty queer, I tell ye. I war trappin' in the Black Hills. It war cold that day, fit to freeze yore breath in chunks. And up on

the peaks where the snow had been a meltin', the water purty nigh froze my feet off. But as I come a-wadin' down hill, purty soon I noticed that the water war gittin' warm, and swift as all get out. I looked ahead and seen steam. Boys, I tell ye, I jumped out o' that crick quicker'n scat — and jest in time. Why, damn my hind-sights if that water hadn't run down hill so fast it was a-bilin' at the bottom!'

... And 'old Gabe,' as his comrades called him, would look round, solemn as a totem pole, wagging his beard at the crowd.

Then some other would enter the arena, and Kit would hear of the giants who lived on an island in the Great Salt Lake, giants who built immense log houses and ate corn from cobs a yard long. What folks thought was forest fires was only the smoke from their pipes.... Kit would hear about the crystal mountain so clear that nobody could see it, so clear that its location and size could only be guessed at from the stacks of bones of animals and birds which had broken their necks by running into it;

about the echo in the Big-horns which took eight hours to return, so that a man on going to bed had only to yell 'Git up!' and next morning promptly the echo would rouse him with a loud 'Git up!'

And someone would narrate the one about the time Bob Hatcher rode under the Spanish Peaks straight into hell and played poker with the old Black Bear himself; about how Broken Hand killed three buffler with one bullet; about the 'putrified' forest where putrified birds sang putrified songs; about the devils who jump up and down in the boiling springs at the foot of Pike's Peak; about the time Jim, or Tom, or Kit shot his mule in mistake for an Injun; about the time old Cotton was cornered by the Blackfoot, with no chance of escape. Old Cotton would dwell upon the hopeless situation. Then he would pause, waiting for his listener to bite. 'Well, what happened?' would come the question. Old Cotton would spit deliberately, roll his cud villainously, and would answer, before exploding in a loud guffaw, 'Why, dang ye, then the Injun killed me!'

The point of the whopper was always that the narrator himself was its hero. No mythical Paul Bunyan could ever have been created among the free and independent trappers. No wage-slaves they, to make a hero of their employer. On the contrary, the *bourgeois*, the boss — with few exceptions — was regarded as quite contemptible. With true Indian brag, each trapper made himself the center of every yarn, however wildly incredible. Yet the joke lay, for these utter realists, in the salty contrast of this crazy individualism with the same common sense of their breed. Their whoppers always appeared perfectly reasonable, perfectly logical, except in one point — a point more logical than all the rest, yet utterly absurd. Their endless lies, their yarns, were the literature of their contempt for the order of the settlements, a justification of their escape to the wild life of the mountains and the plains, where the vastness and haphazard chances of life made logic look a little ridiculous, a little fofurraw.

'Sure, it froze my hair till it was stiff as wire. Sure. I put my hand up to scratch my head, and damned if it didn't come away as full of spines as if I'd stuck it into a porkypine's back. Tuk me all night to get them hairs outen my fist.' And the narrator would scan the back of his hairy paw anxiously. 'Look hyar. Dang me if thar aint some of them hairs still thar! Don't they look the same color as the hair on my head, now?' And the listener would have to guard himself from falling into the trap prepared, so serious was the air of the spinner of yarns.

And then the favorite whopper about the mosquitoes, and how they drove the trapper into his tent. Even there the pests pursued him, pushing their long bills six or eight inches through the canvas. 'And so I thinks to myself, "I'll fix ye, damn ye." And I picked up the axe and went for 'em. Clinched all their bills on the inside of the tent, jest as if they war nails, see? Then I says, "Now, durn ye, buzz yore belly full; I'm goin' to sleep." So I turned in, but purty soon I woke up agin to find the devils bitin' me. And away up yonder against the stars I could see my tent a-sailin' away to the mountings. Durn my skin if them mosquitoes hadn't flew plumb away with tent, and poles, and all!'

In April Kit and his comrades set out on their spring hunt. Now — after the bitter winter — the beaver fur

Mountain Tales

would be at its best. Now their saddle animals, scant of hair but seal-fat after their winter's gnawing on cotton-wood bark, were full of the old ginger and rarin' for the trail. The men loosened their white blanket coats, threw

back the attached capotes, and rode away with heavy packs, trapping the tributaries of Bear River, Green River, in small parties. Kit ran into some of Sinclair's men, learned that Captain Gaunt was in the New Park, decided to take his wages and join him. Kit had seen Gaunt in Taos.

But Kit was an honest man, and Gaunt's shameless cheating of the Indians shook his confidence in his partisan. Kit hired out to Bent and St. Vrain, whose big adobe fort was still building down-river, a few miles above the mouth of the River of Lost Souls, the Purgatoire. There he was put in charge of a gang of loggers, and went into camp on Wild Horse Creek, half a dozen miles below the fort.

Here Kit had his first real battle with Plains Indians, the fight which won him the Indian name by which he was ever after known to the red men.

'One dark night a war party of fifty Crows passed Kit's camp on Wild Horse Creek. As they saw he had only a dozen men and no horse-guard, they quietly rounded up his stock and made off homeward, glad of a chance to ride, since — as was usual in winter — they were all afoot. When morning came, Kit found himself without a single head. But Kit never dreamed of letting them get away with all Bent's stock. He and his dozen men pushed hard along the trail of the thieves, which led off north across the prairie. With them rode two Cheyennes, Black Whiteman and Little Turtle, who had been visiting Kit the night before and had kept their ponies tied up.

'Twilight was falling when Carson's party, the two mounted Cheyennes still out ahead, following the trail in the snow across the prairie, saw a shower of sparks rising from a thicket some distance in front of them. The party halted and held another consultation. Black Whiteman and Little Turtle then rode off alone while Carson drew up his men in a long line, each man several paces from his neighbors on either side.

'As they advanced across the snow a dog barked in the thicket, and a moment later a little ball of white steam shot up from among the willows. The Crows had put out their fire with snow. The Americans quickened their pace and had almost reached the edge of the thicket when without warning sixty Crow warriors broke out of the willows and charged them. So fierce and sudden was the attack

that Carson and his men were borne back and almost surrounded; then they threw up their rifles and gave the Indians a volley.

'Carson used to tell how surprised the Crows were when
they charged in on his little party and were met by a
stunning volley. Back into the thicket went the Crows
and in after them Carson and his men. The Indians
evidently intended to mount and either run away or continue the fight on horseback, but when they reached their
camp in the middle of the thicket they found that the
horses and mules they had left there had disappeared.
Right at their heels came Carson's men; so without halting
the Indians rushed through the thicket and out at the far
side, making off across the prairie as fast as they could go.
The whites, worn out after their long march through the
snow and content with the result of the fight, did not
attempt to follow farther.

'When Carson had started to advance toward the willows, Black Whiteman and Little Turtle had ridden off to
one side, making toward one end of the thicket; then just
as the Crows charged out of the bushes the two Cheyennes
rode in, stampeded the horses and mules and ran them
down the creek.... In the morning Black Whiteman and
Little Turtle returned to the thicket, and there found,
counted *coup* on, and scalped two dead Crows.

'The Cheyennes have always expressed surprise that in
this fight Carson and his men, all well armed and excellent
shots, should have killed only two Crows... not one of
the whites was killed or received a serious wound.'[1]

Kit Carson went to sleep that night tired and hungry,

[1] George Bird Grinnell, *Bent's Old Fort and Its Builders*, Kansas Histori-
cal Society Collections, vol. xv, p. 36.

but with a new confidence. He had killed his first Plains Indian. That fourth brass tack in the stock of his rifle — it counted for more than the other three.

When Yellow Wolf, that wise old chief, brought his band of Cheyennes in to trade at Bent's fort that noon, he talked over the details of the fight with Kit and William Bent, as they sat smoking together in the council room of the half-built fort. With animated gestures and broad grin he taunted the stocky, sandy-haired little white man with his failure to kill more than two Crows. And Kit, knowing what Indian decorum demanded, sat unperturbed and smiled in turn until the chief had had his joke.

Then Yellow Wolf, after a piercing glance at Kit, rose dramatically and gathered his buffalo robe about his hips. He held his chief's pipe along his left arm, and gestured impressively with his right. The white man was young, he was small, his thin hair scarcely reached the shoulders of his white blanket coat; but he was brave, too, and the Cheyennes respected bravery above all things.

The hissing, choking Cheyenne syllables began, the arm and hand swung more vigorously. 'My son, I give you a new name. You have won it. From where the sun now stands your name is *Vih'hiu-nis*, Little Chief.'

That name has stuck to Kit among the Indians to this day.

Big-Foot Wallace Whips His Weight in Wolves

From 'The Adventures of Big-Foot Wallace, the Texas Ranger and Hunter,' by John C. Duval, 1870

'B IG–FOOT WALLACE,' wrote his comrade, 'Texas John' Duval, in 1870, 'is, perhaps, better known throughout Texas as an Indian fighter, hunter, and ranger, than anyone now living in the State; which is saying a good deal, when the great number who have acquired more or less notoriety in that way is taken into consideration. Few men now living, I am confident, have witnessed as many stirring incidents, had more "hairbreadth escapes," or gone through more of the hardships and perils of a border life. He has been a participant in almost every fight, foray, and "scrimmage" with the Mexicans and Indians that has taken place in Texas since he first landed on her shores in 1836.'

W. A. A. Wallace, always known as 'Big-Foot,' was born in Virginia in 1817. At about the age of twenty he came to Texas, and later joined Jack Hays's Company of Texas Rangers, where he met John C. Duval, his future biographer. Wallace, says Webb in *The Texas Rangers*, was 'one of the most original characters in Texas. His giant stature and childlike heart, his drollery and whimsicalness endeared him to the frontier people. His inexhaustible fund of anecdotes and a quaint style of narrative, unspoiled by courses in English composition, made him welcome by every fireside.' He remained all his life on the Frontier, defending the settlements, and, in spite of many wild and dramatic adventures, lived until 1899.

The Adventures of Big-Foot Wallace, the Texas Ranger and Hunter, by John C. Duval, was published in Philadelphia in 1870. Perhaps it is ungracious to call it a fictional biography, in the light of the author's modest claim to 'at least one *merit*, not often found in similar publications — it is not a compilation of imaginary scenes and incidents, concocted in the brain of one who never was beyond the sound of a dinner-bell in his life, but a plain, unvarnished story of the "'scapes and scrapes" of Big-Foot Wallace, the Texas Ranger and Hunter, written out from notes furnished by himself, and told, as well as my memory serves me, in his own language.'

The following story is from Chapter XII of the second edition, 1873.

Big-Foot Wallace Whips His Weight in Wolves

HAVE I ever told you, asked Big-Foot, about the 'tussle' I had with the wolves a short time after I came to Texas? It was a sort of initiation fee paid for my entrance into the mysteries of border life, and I don't think I have ever been as badly frightened before or since. It happened in this way:

One very cold evening, two or three hours, perhaps, before sundown, I concluded to take a little round in the woods, by way of exercise, and bring home some fresh venison for supper; so I picked up 'Sweet-Lips,' [1] and started for a rough, broken piece of country, where previously I had always found deer in abundance. But, somehow, the deer didn't seem to be stirring that evening, and I walked two or three miles without finding a single one. After going so far, I hated to return without meat, and I kept on, still hoping to find the deer before it got too dark to shoot; but at last I had to give it up, and turned my course back toward home again.

By this time the sun was setting, and I hurried up as fast as possible, to get out of the chaparral and into the prairie before night came on. All the evening I had heard the wolves howling around in an unusual way, but I had

[1] His rifle.

no fear of them, as I had been told they seldom, if ever, attacked a man in Texas. When I had gone back perhaps a half mile or so, a large gray wolf trotted out into the path before me, and commenced howling in the most mournful manner; and, in an instant, he was answered by a dozen other wolves in the hills around us. Thinks I, old fellow, if you are hatching a plot for my benefit, I'll make sure of you, anyhow; so I brought 'Sweet-Lips' to range on his shoulder-blade, and at the crack of the gun he gave one spring into the air, and dropped as dead as a hammer in his tracks.

But somehow, although I can't say I felt any fear of them, my suspicions were aroused as to foul play on the part of the gentlemen who were answering him from the hills, and I loosened 'Old Butch' in the sheath, rammed another bullet down 'Sweet-Lips,' and as soon as I had done so, I put out for home again in double-quick time. But the faster I went, the faster the wolves followed me, and, looking back after a little while, I saw twenty-five or thirty 'lobos' (a large, fierce kind of wolf, found only in Mexico and Texas) trotting along after me at a rate I knew would soon bring them into close quarters; and in the bushes and chaparral, that bordered the trail I was traveling, I could see the gleaming eyes and pointed ears of at least a dozen others coming rapidly toward me.

I saw in a minute that they meant mischief, but I knew it was useless to try to beat a wolf in a foot-race. However, I resolved to keep on as long as they would let me, and when they closed in, that I would give them the best ready-made fight I had 'in the shop.' So I stepped out as briskly as I could, and the wolves trotted after me, howling in a way that made my hair stand on end and my very blood run cold. A dozen times I wished myself back again safe in 'Old Virginny,' where a man might travel for a hundred miles without meeting up with anything more dangerous than a 'possum; but wishing didn't stop the wolves, so I let out my 'best licks,' hoping that I could make home before they could muster up courage enough to attack me.

But, I 'reckoned without my host,' for one big fellow, more daring or hungry than the rest, made a rush at me, and I barely had time to level my gun and fire, for he was touching the muzzle of it when I pulled the trigger. He fell dead at my feet, but, as if this had been the signal for a general attack, in an instant the whole pack were around me, snarling and snapping, and showing their white teeth in a way that was anything but pleasant.

I fought them off with the breech of my gun, for they didn't give me any chance to load it, retreating all the while as rapidly as I could. Once so many of them rushed in upon me at the same time that, in spite of all my efforts, I failed to keep them at bay, and they dragged me to the ground. I thought for an instant that it was all up with me, but despair gave me the strength of half a dozen men, and I used 'Old Butch' to such a good purpose that I killed three outright and wounded several others, which appeared somewhat to daunt the balance, for they drew off a short distance and began to howl for reinforcements.

The reinforcements were on their way, for I could hear them howling in every direction, and I knew that I had no time to lose. So I put off at the top of my speed, and in those days it took a pretty fast Spanish pony to beat me a quarter when I 'let out the kinks.' I let 'em out this time with a will, I tell you, and fairly beat the wolves for half a mile or so, but my breath then began to fail me, and I could tell by their close, angry yelps that the devils were again closing in upon me.

By this time I was so much exhausted that I knew I should make a poor fight of it, more especially as I could perceive, from the number of dark forms behind me, and the gleaming eyes and shining teeth that glistened out of every bush on the wayside, that the wolves had had a considerable addition to their number. It may be thought strange that I didn't 'take to a tree,' but there were no trees there to take to — nothing but stunted chaparral bushes, not much higher than a man's head.

I thought my time had come at last, and I was almost ready to give up in despair, when all at once I remembered seeing, as I came out, a large lone oak tree, with a hollow in it about large enough for a man to crawl into, which grew on the banks of a small cañon not more than three or four hundred yards from where I then was. I resolved to make one more effort, and, if possible, to reach this tree before the wolves came up with me again; and if ever there was good, honest running done, without any throw-off about it, I did it then. The fact is, I believe a man can't tell how fast he can run until he gets a pack of wolves after him in this way. A fellow will naturally do his best when he knows that, if he doesn't, in twenty minutes he will be 'parceled out' among as many ravenous wolves, a head to one, a leg to another, an arm to a third, and so on. At least that was the effect it had on me, and I split the air so fast with my nose that it took the skin off of it, and for a week after it looked like a peeled onion.

However, I beat the wolves once more fairly and squarely, and not much time to spare either, for just as I crawled into the hollow of the tree (which was about as high as my head from the ground), the ravenous creatures were howling all around me. At the bottom of the hollow I found a skunk snugly stowed away, but I soon routed him out, and the wolves gobbled him up in an instant. He left a smell behind him, though, that was anything but agreeable in such close quarters. However, I was safe there, at any rate, from the attacks of the wolves, and all the smells in the city of New Orleans couldn't have driven me from my hole just at that time.

The wolves could only get at me one at a time, and with 'Old Butch' in my hand, I knew I could manage a hundred in that way. But such howling and yelling I never heard before or since but once, and that was when I was with the Keechies, and a runner came in and told them their great chief, 'Buffalo Hump,' had been killed in a fight with the Lipans! They bit, and gnawed, and scratched, but it wasn't any use, and every now and then a fellow would jump up and poke his nose into the hollow of the tree; but just as sure as he did it, he caught a wipe across it with

'Old Butch' that generally satisfied his curiosity for a while. All night long they kept up their serenade, and, as you may well suppose, I didn't get much sleep. However, the noise didn't matter, for I had got several severe bites on my arms and legs, and the pain I suffered from them would have kept me awake anyhow.

Just at daylight the next morning the wolves began to sneak off, and when the sun rose not one was to be seen, except three dead ones at the root of the tree, that had come in contact with 'Old Butch.' I waited a while longer, to be certain they had all left, when I crawled out of my den, gave myself a shake, and found I was all right, except a pound or so of flesh taken out of one of my legs, and a few scratches on my arms. I hobbled back home; and for a long time afterward, whenever I heard the howling of wolves, I always felt a little uneasy.

I found out, the next day, why the wolves had attacked me in the way they did. I had a bottle of asafoetida in my trunk, which somehow had got broken and run out among my clothes, and when the wolves pitched into me I had on a coat that had been wet with the confounded stuff, and smelt worse than a polecat. I had often heard that asafoetida would attract wolves, but I always thought, before this, that it was a sort of old-woman's yarn; but it's a fact, and if you don't believe it, go some dark night into a thick chaparral, where wolves are numerous, and pour about a gill over your coat, and then wait a little, and see what will turn up; and if you don't hear howling, and snapping, and snarling, I'll agree to be stung to death by bumble-bees.

Big-Foot and the Wolves

The Fight in the Canyon

From 'The Adventures of Big-Foot Wallace, the Texas Ranger and Hunter, by John C. Duval, 1870

The Fight in the Canyon

'**W**ELL, how was it, Big-Foot,' I asked, 'about that fight you had with the big Indian in the cañon?'

'The fact is, sir,' said he, 'I caught a tremendous cold last night, and I'm so hoarse now I can hardly talk at all. I've got this cabin chinked entirely too tight' — looking around at the cracks, through which the stars could be seen twinkling in every direction — 'and I shall have to knock out some more of the "daubin." Nothing like a tight room to give a man a cold. When I went on to the "States," five or six years ago, I had a cold constantly from sleeping in rooms that were as tight as a bottle. People want a supply of fresh air just as much as they do their regular meals, and occasionally something to clear the cobwebs out of their throats.' And as he said this, Big-Foot looked longingly toward the corner of the cabin in which the jug was deposited.

I took the hint, and handed over the 'red-eye,' when he glued the mouth of the jug affectionately to his lips, took an observation of the stars through one of the chinks for about half a minute, and then setting it down with a long breath, he wiped his lips on the cuff of his hunting-shirt, deliberately drew his butcher-knife from its sheath, cut a section from a plug of tobacco, crammed it into his mouth, and giving a preliminary squirt, to see if his spitting apparatus was all in good trim, he began his yarn of the 'struggle for life.'

In the fall of '42, the Indians were worse on the frontiers than they had ever been before, or since. You couldn't stake a horse out at night with any expectation of finding him the next morning, and a fellow's scalp wasn't safe on his head five minutes outside of his own shanty. The people on the frontiers at last came to the conclusion that something had to be done, or else they would be compelled to fall back on the 'settlements,' which you know would have been reversing the natural order of things. So we collected together by agreement at my ranch, organized a company of about forty men, and the next time the Indians came down from the mountains (and we hadn't long to wait for them), we took the trail, determined to follow it as long as our horses would hold out.

The trail led us up toward the head waters of the Llano, and the third day out I noticed a great many 'signal smokes' rising up a long way off in the direction we were traveling. These 'signal smokes' are very curious things anyhow. You will see them rise up in a straight column (no matter how hard the wind may be blowing), and after reaching a great height they will spread out at the top like an umbrella, and then, in a minute or so, puff! they are all gone in the twinkling of an eye. How the Indians make them, I never could learn, and I have often asked old frontiersmen if they could tell me, but none of them could ever give me any information on the subject. Even the white men who have been captured by the Indians, and lived with them for years, never learned how these 'signal smokes' were made.

Well, as I was saying, on the third day out we found Indian 'signs' as plentiful as pig-tracks around a corn-crib, and I told the captain we would have to move very cautiously, or we would be apt to find ourselves, before long, in a hornets' nest. That night we camped at a water-hole, and put out a double guard. Just before the sun went down, I had noticed a smoke, apparently about three miles to the northeast of us, and felt satisfied that there was a party of Indians encamped at that place. So I went to the captain and told him, if he would give me leave to do so, I would get up an hour or two before day-light and reconnoiter the position, and find out whether there were any Indians there or not, and if so, to what tribe they belonged, what was their number, etc. He was willing enough to let me go, and told the guards to pass me out whenever I wanted to leave.

I whetted up 'Old Butcher' a little, rammed two bullets down the throat of 'Sweet-Lips,' and about two hours before daylight I left camp and started off in the direction of the smoke I had seen the evening before. The chaparral, in some places, was as thick as the hair on a dog's back, but I 'scuffled' through it in the dark, and after traveling perhaps a mile and a half, I came to a deep cañon, that seemed to head up in the direction I had seen the smoke. I scrambled down into it and waited until day began to break, and then slowly and cautiously continued my course along the bottom of the cañon.

The cañon was very crooked, and in some places so narrow that there was hardly room enough in it for two men to travel abreast. At length I came to a place where it made a sudden bend to the left, and just as I turned the corner I came plump up against a big Indian, who was coming down the cañon, I suppose, with the intention of spying out our camp. We were both stooping down when we met, and our heads came together with considerable force, and the Indian rolled one way and I the other.

Both rose about the same time, and so unexpected was the encounter that we stood for a moment uncertain what to do, and glaring upon each other like two catamounts when they are about to dispute the carcass of a dead deer. The Indian had a gun as well as I, but we were too close to each other to shoot, and it seemed we both came to the same instant, for we dropped our rifles, and grappled each other without saying a word.

You see, boys, I am a pretty stout man yet, but in those days, without meaning to brag, I don't believe there was a white man west of the Colorado River that could stand up against me in a regular catamount, bear-hug, hand-to-hand fight. But the minute I 'hefted' that Indian, I knew I had undertaken a job that would bring the sweat from me (and maybe so, I thought, a little blood too) before it was satisfactorily finished. He was nearly as tall as I am, say six feet one or two inches, and would weigh, I suppose, about one hundred and seventy-five pounds net, for he had no clothes on worth mentioning. I had the advantage of him in weight, but he was as wiry and active as a cat and as slick as an eel, and no wonder, either, for he was greased from head to foot with bear's oil.

At it we went, in right down earnest, without a word being spoken by either of us, first up one side of the cañon, then down in the bottom, then up the other side, and the dust and gravel flew in such a way that if anyone had been

The Fight in the Canyon

passing along the bank above, he would have supposed that a small whirlwind was raging below. I was a little the stronger of the two, however, and whenever we rose to our feet I could throw the Indian easily enough, but the moment he touched the ground, the 'varmint' would give himself a sort of a squirm, like a snake, and pop right up on top of me, and I couldn't hold him still a moment, he was so slick with bear's grease. Each of us was trying to draw his butcher-knife from the sheath all the time, but we kept each other so busy, neither could get a chance to do it.

At last, I found that my breath began to fail me, and came to the conclusion, if something wasn't done pretty soon, I should 'have my note taken' to a certainty, for the Indian was like a lobos wolf, and was getting better the longer he fought. So the next time we rose, I put out all the strength I had left in me, and gave him a 'back-handed trip' that brought his head with great force against a sharp-pointed rock upon the ground. He was completely stunned by the shock for an instant, and before he fairly came to, I snatched my knife from the sheath, and drove it with all my strength up to the hilt in his body. The moment he felt the cold steel, he threw me off of him as if I had been a ten-year-old boy, sprang upon me before I could rise, drew his own butcher-knife, and raised it above his head with the intention of plunging it into my breast.

I tell you what, boys, I often see that Indian now in my dreams (particularly after eating a hearty supper of bear's meat and honey), grappling me by the throat with his left hand, and the glittering butcher-knife lifted up above me in his right, and his two fierce black eyes gleaming like a panther's in the dark! Under such circumstances, it is astonishing how fast a man will think. He thinks faster than the words can fly over those 'new-fangled' telegraph lines. I looked up to the blue sky, and bid it a long farewell, and to the green trees, the sparkling waters, and the bright sun. Then I thought of my mother, as I remembered her when I was a little boy, the 'old home,' the apple orchard, the brook where I used to fish for minnows, and the 'commons,' where I used to ride every stray donkey and pony I could catch; and then I thought of Alice Ann, a blue-eyed, partridge-built young woman I had a 'leaning to,' who lived down in the Zumwalt Settlement. All these, and many more thoughts besides, flashed through my mind in the little time that knife was gleaming above my breast.

All at once the Indian gave a keen yell, and down came the knife with such force that it was buried to the hilt in the hard earth close to my side. The last time I had thrown the Indian, a deep gash had been cut in his forehead by the sharp-pointed rock, and the blood running down into his eyes from the wound blinded him, so that he missed his aim. I fully expected him to repeat his blow, but he lay still, and made no attempt to draw the knife from the ground. I looked at his eyes, and they were closed hard and fast, but there was a devilish sort of grin still about his mouth, as if he had died under the belief that he had sent me before him into the 'happy hunting grounds.'

I threw him off of me, and he rolled to the bottom of the cañon 'stone dead.' My knife had gone directly to his heart. I looked at him sometime, lying there so still, and stiffening fast in the cool morning air, and I said to myself, 'Well, old fellow, you made a good fight of it anyhow, and if luck hadn't been against you, you would have "taken my sign in," too, to a certainty, and Alice Ann would have lost the best string she's got to her bow.

'And now,' said I to myself, 'old fellow, I am going to do for you what I never did for an Indian before. I am going to give you a decent Christian burial.' So I broke his gun into a dozen pieces and laid them beside him, according to the Indian custom, so it might be handy for him when he got to the happy hunting grounds (though if they haven't first-rate smiths there, I don't think it will be fit for use soon), and then I pulled up some pieces of rock from the sides of the cañon, and piled them around and over him until he was completely covered, and safe from the attacks of coyotes and other animals, and there, I have no doubt, his bones are to this day.

John Henry

*From 'John Henry: Tracking Down a
Negro Legend' by G. B. Johnson, 1929*

THE Civil War is over, the Heroic Age is waning, the railroad is twisting into the heart of the backwoods, and the end of the Frontier is in sight. In the Big Bend Tunnel, piercing the Alleghenies of West Virginia, lies John Henry, steel-driver, dead with his hammer in his hand. The old pioneers have vanished, but a new hero legend has been born.

John Henry is probably the greatest of the Negro folk idols. A far cry from the cunning, alert backwoodsman, he represents brute strength and dumb courage. His great feat was to beat a steam-drill in driving holes in the rock for dynamite. He outdrove the drill, but it killed him. It was a dying triumph of man over the machine.

The forms of the John Henry myth show endless variety. Guy B. Johnson, in *John Henry: Tracking Down a Negro Legend* (University of North Carolina Press, 1929), has dipped deeply into the whole subject, questioning the hundreds of persons who think that they worked — or that their fathers or uncles or grandfathers worked — with John Henry, collecting over fifty variants of the legend, weighing the evidence of the many localities that claim him, determining his position in the living tradition of today. Was he man or myth? No one can say for sure; nor does it greatly matter. The significant fact is that the John Henry legend has spread the length and breadth of the land, that 'his name is sung from a thousand dusky lips every day.'

John Henry was first celebrated in hammer-songs, whose short verses were sung to the rhythm of a pick or a nine-pound sledge. Later, as the story grew, came the rather longer and more formal ballads. The ballad here is reprinted from Mr. Johnson's book with the permission of the publisher. Mr. Johnson notes that this 'unusual version... contributed by Leon R. Harris of Moline, Illinois... is the Virginia and West Virginia version.'

John Henry

LISSEN to my story;
   'Tis a story true;
   'Bout a mighty man — John Henry was his name,
An' John Henry was a steel-driver too —
Lawd — Lawd —
John Henry was a steel-driver too.

John Henry had a hammah;
Weighed nigh fo'ty poun';
Eb'ry time John made a strike
He seen his steel go 'bout two inches down —
Lawd — Lawd —
He seen his steel go 'bout two inches down.

John Henry's woman, Lucy —
Dress she wore was blue;
Eyes like stars an' teeth lak-a marble stone,
An' John Henry named his hammah 'Lucy' too —
Lawd — Lawd —
John Henry named his hammah 'Lucy' too.

Lucy came to see him;
Bucket in huh han';

All th' time John Henry ate his snack,
O Lucy she'd drive steel lak-a man —
Lawd — Lawd —
O Lucy she'd drive steel lak-a man.

John Henry's cap'n Tommy —
V'ginny gave him birth;
Loved John Henry like his only son,
And Cap' Tommy was the whitest man on earth —
Lawd — Lawd —
Cap' Tommy was th' whitest man on earth.

One day Cap' Tommy told him
How he'd bet a man;
Bet John Henry'd beat a steam-drill down,
Jes' cause he was th' best in th' lan' —
Lawd — Lawd —
'Cause he was th' best in th' lan'.

John Henry tol' Cap' Tommy;
Lightnin' in his eye;
'Cap'n, bet yo' las' red cent on me,
Fo' I'll beat it to th' bottom or I'll die —
Lawd — Lawd —
I'll beat it to th' bottom or I'll die.

'Co'n pone's in my stomach;
Hammah's in my han';
Hain't no steam-drill on dis railroad job
Can beat "Lucy" an' her steel-drivin' man,
Lawd — Lawd —
Can beat "Lucy" an' her steel-drivin' man.

'Bells ring on de engines;
Runnin' down th' line;
Dinnahs done when Lucy pulls th' co'd;
But no hammah in this mountain rings like mine —
Lawd — Lawd —
No hammah in this mountain rings like mine.'

Sun shined hot an' burnin'
Wer'n't no breeze at-tall;
Sweat ran down like watah down a hill
That day John Henry let his hammah fall —
Lawd — Lawd —
That day John Henry let his hammah fall.

John Henry kissed his hammah;
White man turned on steam;
Li'l' Bill held John Henry's trusty steel —

'Twas th' biggest race th' worl' had ever seen —
Lawd — Lawd —
Th' biggest race th' worl' had ever seen.

White man tol' John Henry —
'Niggah, dam yo' soul,
You might beat dis steam an' drill o' mine
When th' rocks in this mountain turn to gol' —
Lawd — Lawd —
When th' rocks in this mountain turn to gol'.'

John Henry tol' th' white man;
Tol' him kind-a sad:
'Cap'n George I want-a be yo' fr'en;
If I beat yo' to th' bottom, don't git mad —
Lawd — Lawd —
If I beat yo' to th' bottom, don't git mad.'

Cap' Tommy sees John Henry's
Steel a-bitin' in;
Cap'n slaps John Henry on th' back,
Says, 'I'll give yo' fifty dollars if yo' win —
Lawd — Lawd —
I'll give yo' fifty dollars if yo' win.'

White man saw John Henry's
Steel a-goin' down;
White man says — 'That man's a mighty man,
But he'll weaken when th' hardes' rock is foun' —
Lawd — Lawd —
He'll weaken when th' hardes' rock is foun'.

John Henry

John Henry, O John Henry —
John Henry's hammah too;
When a woman's 'pendin' on a man
Hain't no tellin' what a mighty man can do —
Lawd — Lawd —
No tellin' what a mighty man can do.

John Henry, O John Henry!
Blood am runnin' red!
Falls right down with his hammah to th' groun',
Says, 'I've beat him to th' bottom but I'm dead —
Lawd — Lawd —
I've beat him to th' bottom but I'm dead.'

John Henry kissed his hammah;
Kissed it with a groan;
Sighed a sigh an' closed his weary eyes,
Now po' Lucy has no man to call huh own —
Lawd — Lawd —
Po' Lucy has no man to call huh own.

Cap' Tommy came a-runnin'
To John Henry's side;
Says, 'Lawd, Lawd — O Lawdy, Lawdy, Lawd —
He's beat it to th' bottom but he's died —
Lawd — Lawd —
He's beat it to th' bottom but he's died.'

Lucy ran to see him;
Dress she wore was blue;
Started down th' track an' she nevvah did turn back,

Sayin', 'John Henry, I'll be true — true to you —
Lawd — Lawd —
John Henry, I'll be true — true to you.'

John Henry, O John Henry!
Sing it if yo' can —
High an' low an' ev'ry where yo' go —
He died with his hammah in his han' —
Lawd — Lawd —
He died with his hammah in his han'.

Buddie, where'd yo' come from
To this railroad job?
If yo' wantta be a good steel-drivin' man,
Put yo' trus' in yo' hammah an' yo' God —
Lawd — Lawd —
Put yo' trus' in yo' hammah an' yo' God.

Paul Bunyan Comes West

By Ida Virginia Turney, 1920, 1928

THERE is no more glorious cycle of tall tales than those of Paul Bunyan and Babe the Blue Ox. Like the John Henry ballads, they belong to the last phase of the Frontier. No one knows just where they began, but certainly they show kinship to the more fantastic of the earlier backwoods yarns. Esther Shephard, in her *Paul Bunyan* (Harcourt, Brace, 1924), finds it likely that 'part of this stream of western humor which filled such a large part of the literature of those early days, crowded out of the main channel by the excitement of the Civil War time, may have found its outlet in the logging camps in the great Northern Woods and turned itself naturally into the Paul Bunyan legends.' Though they probably reached their height during the eighties and nineties, they are still alive today.

These logging myths were handed down by word of mouth for many generations before they appeared in print. The first Paul Bunyan book was Ida Virginia Turney's *Paul Bunyan Comes West*, published by the University of Oregon in 1920 and — with additions — by Houghton Mifflin Company in 1928. A shortened form of the latter book is printed here. In her foreword Miss Turney writes: 'The tales of the doings of the master woodsman Paul Bunyan were first told by "lumberjacks" who "go to the woods" in the long winters, and "on the drive" when spring unleashes the rivers to carry the logs in foaming jaws to the sawmill towns in the valleys. They told them wherever of evenings they gathered about the "deacon-seat" in the bunk-shanty, dank with the steam of mackinaws strung to dry above the red-hot stove and reeking with the odor of Peerless and Star. And later they passed them on to the gangs that followed the line of the "clearing" as it moved westward from New England to Alaska — opening mines, piercing mountains with steel rails, taming the cattle of the hills, or flinging bridges over rivers and canyons.'

Paul Bunyan Comes West

YEH, I knowed Paul Bunyan. My father worked fer him when I wuz a leetle shaver an' I uster allus tag 'long. Logger? Wal, I sh'd say — cut m' teeth on a peevy an' rolled logs in m' first long pants. 'Twuz some loggin' them days — trees all round here twelve t' fourteen foot thru.

Paul he come to Oregon round by Californy 'count o' a mistake an' that thar blamed train is follered consid'able yit. Y' see Paul wuz a busy man an' when he wuz in a special hurry he didn't never stop fer no train; he jist hoofed 'er — in winter he done it on snowshoes. 'Twuz the winter o' the Blue Snow, the same year's the rain come up from China an' tore all the roots of the alfalfy up an' the' wuz big floods all over the hull kentry. That year Paul he jist finished up his loggin' job in Dakoty an' he thought he'd take a look at the West. 'Nother thing, with the trees all gone the weather got awful cold. One mornin' when Paul wuz a-gittin' himself some breakfast he set the coffee pot full o' bilin' coffee on the back o' the stove fer a minute an' it froze so fast the durned ice wuz too hot to handle. Wal, that settled it fer Paul — the West fer hisn. When he wuz leavin' Minnesoty the' wuz a lot o' snow in the woods yit, so he jist stropped on his snowshoes an' struck out straight west. 'Fore long the sun got awful hot an' the dust riz in clouds, but Paul he kept a-goin'. Bymby it got so durned hot it warped Paul's snowshoes somethin' turrible — the left un a lot more'n the right — so's he traveled in a arc an' come out at 'Frisco, nine hundred miles outn his way, an' he lost a hull day by it.

Paul he wuz a-totin' his big pick an' shovel 'long in case he sh'd run right onto pay dirt, an' he come to a place whar he thought he c'd fix a good waterin' place fer Babe. Wal, he dug an' dug till the bottom fell outn that thar hole, an' he wuz so s'prized he let go his shovel an' it dropped clean out o' sight. Paul he jist about give up ever gittin' it back; but in about an hour er so, it struck awful hard rock an' bounded clean back outn the hole an' up in the air more'n a hundred feet. 'Course Paul never could ketch it, fer it wuz all melted; so it's been boundin' up an' down faithful once an hour ever since. Bym-by the Gov'ment named the hole Old Faithful an' put the Yellowstone National Park 'round it.

Paul went 'long totin' jist the pick, but by the aft'noon o' the second day it begun to git kind o' heavy. Then he come to the Colorado River an' he thought he'd wade 'long upstream fer a spell an' cool his feet. He drug the pick 'long behind him fer to ease his shoulder an' it made quite a scratch in the river bed, tho it wuz runnin' thru solid rock. Fust thing Paul knowed he c'd hardly see out. That thar scratch they calls the Colorado Canyon.

I dunno whar Paul fust settled in the West, but I reckin purty much all over. Sartin they all claims him. The Blue Snow wuz worser an' deeper in British Columbia an' Washington 'n it'd been in Dakoty, an' it wuz bluer, too, awful blue, jist the color o' the deep sea. The women-

Paul Bunyan, Master Woodsman

folks they used a leetle mite o' it in the rinse water fer bluin' an' some o' 'em melted it down fer ink. Paul he had a bar'l o' it. Wal, Paul he went 'long up the Snoqualmie Pass that winter an' built a camp on the Skomackaway with all the modern fixin's. 'Stead o' the big griddle like he had in the Dakoty camp he set up a steel-topped range seven block long. The' wuz a cook to each block an' twenty boys with slabs o' bacon tied onto their feet to keep it greased. The hot-cake batter wuz mixed up in tanks sixty foot square an' carried to the stove on cranes swung careful, so's the boys'd have plenty o' time to git off when the stream started. Wunst er twicet in Dakoty — wal, they wuz kinda out o' luck. Ever'thing in that thar camp wuz bran' new, even to the dinner horn. Paul he wuz bound to blow the horn jist fer to try the tone. The boys all warned him not to, but he done it anyway, an' fust blast down come three sections o' timber. Paul orter knowed better, fer he done the same thing in Kansas an' the timber never growed up agin *thar*.

A feller by the name o' Murphy tells 'bout how Paul found his wife in the heart o' a great white pine an' didn't never let no one see her, but 'taint so. Paul's wife wuz reg'lar folks, an' she never set in no moonlight spoonin' with Paul. She cooked fer three hundred men, usin' a donkey boiler with the top tore off fer to bile beans in when extry hands wuz needed.

Paul sent fer his big Blue Ox, Babe, after he got out West. He wuz a 'normous critter — forty axe-handles and a plug o' Star terbacker between the eyes. Paul he allus toted 'long a field-glass with him so's he could see what Babe wuz a-doin' with his hind feet. Babe had a awful

appetite, 'specially fer hot-cakes, an' he *could* eat baled
hay; but he had to have one er tother an' a lot o' it. An'
drink — say, the's lakes all over the hull kentry whar
Paul dug waterin' holes fer him. When Paul an' Babe got

BABE

to the bank o' the Skomackaway, an' camped, the' wuzn't
no hot-cakes ner baled hay to be got. They thought they
could fool Babe with Shredded Wheat Buscuit, but he
knowed he wuzn't gittin' nothin'; an' as soon as Paul let
him out to graze he fell to an' et up forty er fifty acres o'
good Douglas fir.

Purty soon 'long come the Forest Ranger an' ordered
Paul fer to tie Babe up 'fore he rooned the lumber business.

Paul he sez, 'I don't aim to make no onnecessary
trouble, but I ain't got nothin' to tie him with.'

'Thar's a big ship anchor chain,' sez the Ranger.
'That'd orter do.'

'Guess she'll do,' sez Paul. 'But what'll I tie him to?'

An' the Ranger he sez, 'Y' kin try tyin' him to that thar rock; guess that'll ballast him.'

Wal, Paul he wuz some juberous, but he wuz willin' to try; so he tied Babe to the rock an' went to bed. 'Long toward mornin' he heard a turrible ruckus an' he got up an' found Babe a-pawin' the ground an' snortin' somethin' awful. Paul he tried to quiet him, but no-sir-ee, he'd got a whiff o' hot-cakes cookin' over in Vancouver an' thar wuzn't no holdin' him. He give one beller an' out come the rock. An' the hole it left filled up with water an' made Lake Washington. The next day when Paul wuz atrakin' him he found a big waterfall in the Skomackaway River whar Babe had pawed up the bed when he crost it, an' named it Snoqualmie Falls. On a piece further Babe dropped a part o' the dirt he'd drug 'long — an' that's Mount Li. An' the rock he wuz hitched to — wal, when that thar anchor chain busted it flew off an' kept goin' a spell 'fore it settled, an' afterwards a feller named it Mount Ranier. Yeh, Paul wuz purty well satisfied with what Babe'd turned off in a day; but when he heard that that thar beller capsized six steamers offin the coast an' all hands drowned, he wuz some distressed. An' after all Babe wuzn't pacified; thar wuzn't but a hundred men in the Vancouver camp an' not 'nough hot-cakes made to more'n whet up his appetite.

Babe wuz allus playful. He liked to kick up mud-pies gin'ally, an' sometimes he mussed up the landscape consid'able an' Paul wouldn't 'low him no hot-cakes for a spell. One time Babe wuz a feelin' awful gay — he'd et fifteen hot-cakes cooked over the hull stove, an' all the baled Shredded Wheat in camp, then he tackled the fodder

outn two silos belongin' to a neighbor o' Paul's — so he
scampered off to make mud-pies. He come to a big mud-
puddle an' begun to dig a outlet to the sea. He kicked all
the dirt into a pan he'd drug 'long. 'Bout that time Paul
missed him an' started after him. Babe seen him comin'
an' he jist dropped the pan an' legged it fer home. Wal,
he never got a chanct to go back fer no pan, an' bym-by
the dirt in it all wooded over an' made a island — folks
call it Vancouver.

Paul's gang cleared a lot o' dirt outn Gray's Harbor with
a Bagley scraper seventy-three feet wide; but he never
not to say worked till he got into the Comp'ny. He'd
heard 'bout Dan Puget an' Ol' Man Elliott an' Dad Hood,
an' they'd heard consid'able 'bout him an' the Blue Ox.
One day a gang o' Dan's men wuz out a-scoutin' round in
Washington an' they come to Rock Crick an' couldn't git
crost it, 'cause it wuz swelled with the snow that'd melted
an' roarin' 'long terrific. So they sent down to Skomackaway fer help to build a bridge. Paul he come up an'

looked her over. 'Give me a day an' a half,' he sez, 'an' I'll have a bridge fer you.' Wal, they fixed fer to camp thar a month er so.

Next day Paul he went on up the crick a ways to whar the' wuz a nice straight red cedar seven foot thru fer seventy foot 'bove ground, an' right crost the stream wuz a sharp-pinted rock. Wal, Paul he jist felled that thar tree onto the rock, an' she split open clean's cheese an' made a bridge fourteen foot wide, an' the hull gang got crost 'thout losin' a day.

Levi Lugg wuz Paul's handy man when he logged up the Mackenzie, an' he never laid down on no job. He uster bring in the firewood on the calks o' his boots, an' he could swing Paul's double-bladed axe most as good as Paul could — but not quite. That thar ace had a wove grass handle, an' Paul he jist swung it round in a circle an' cut all the trees in reach to wunst.

Paul didn't have no book-larnin'; so when he wanted anythin' to the store he jist drawed a pitcher o' it, an' gin'lly he got what he sent fer. But one time he didn't. Levi wuz a-goin' to town an' Paul thought it'd be a good chanst to send fer a grindstone; so he drawed a circle on a paper an' give it to Levi to give to the storekeeper. Next day when Levi got back an' ondone his pack he didn't have no grindstone — had a cheese 'stead o' it. 'Wal,' sez Paul, 'if I didn't fergit to put the hole in the durned thing.' An' right thar Paul he sez, 'I'm a-goin' to have me a Unerversity' — an' he done it.

The biggest job o' loggin' Paul ever done in Oregon wuz the winter o' the Blue Snow. He had a camp on the Columbia River same's on the Skomackaway an' kept his eye on both. Paul he had some bad luck in the Oregon camp. He driv the logs plum over the Columbia River Falls an' then he see he'd got the wrong logs an' had to drive 'em all back.

After Paul got the south side o' Mount Hood all logged off, he hitched his Blue Ox to his heavy plow, the one that'd turn forty acre to two furrers, an' started in breakin' it fer plantin'. But he didn't git much done, fer Babe he stepped into a yeller-jacket's nest an' run away draggin' the plow 'long. The gash he made in the hills folks calls the Columbia River Gorge. Paul he never did colleck the pieces o' that thar plow.

An' Paul tried ranchin', tho loggin' wuz more in his line. I guess ever'body's heard 'bout the hard luck he had in Kansas. Some crook sold him a farm an' the soil wuz so rich nobody ever dast plant anythin' on it. Paul he went out fer to look it over an' on the way he dropped a kernel o' corn, an' by the time he'd went a few steps that thar corn wuz knee-high. He run to the house fer to git Sweede Charlie to watch it grow, an' by the time they got back it wuz higher'n their heads. Paul he figgered to cut the top off an' stop it growin', so he sent Charlie up the stalk, but he couldn't git to the top; an' when he tried to slide down he couldn't neither, fer it growed faster'n he c'd slide. He liked to starved till Paul loaded up his shotgun with doughnuts an' shot 'em up to him. Then 'long come the Gov'ment Inspector an' sez: 'Paul, y' got to git that corn-stalk down; it's drainin' the Mississippi River dry an' interferin' with navigation.' Fin'lly Paul he sent fer a couple o' rails 'bout a mile long an' knotted 'em together round the stalk by runnin' Babe round it, an' the faster it

Paul Bunyan and Babe the Blue Ox

growed the more it cut itself. Jist then 'long come a cyclone an' finished it.

Y' ever see that cleared spot — 'bout a hundred acres — up the Mackenzie River? Wal, that thar wuz Paul's ranch. He cal'lated to raise wheat on 't; so he built a tight board fence round it an' sowed it to wheat. It jist got started an' a big hail-storm come on an' beat it into the ground. So Paul he planted it over ag'in, an' as soon's it got 'bout ripe 'long come a herd o' elk an' jumped the fence an' milled round an' tromped it all out. Wal, sir, both o' them seedin's 'd took, an' the grain wuz so heavy it run clean over the second board o' the fence.

Paul had his worst luck when he went into the hog business in Eastern Oregon. An' it wuzn't his fault neither. His ranch wuz clean back in the mountains an' the' wuzn't no road cut. He jist got a nice start an' somethin' begun to take the hogs — fifteen, twenty a night — an' fin'lly the corn begun to go, too. Paul seen some bear tracks an' he follered 'em thirty mile to a cave in Box Canyon; an' thar he found his hogs all fattened an' killed, an' the corn all stored in ricks. Wal, the buildin' o' the road to haul the meat out after it wuz cured et up all the profit — an' then some.

'Bout this time Babe come to an on-timely end. Paul an' his family wuz a-spendin' the week-end at the camp on the Skomackaway an' Babe wuz 'long. He got hungry fer hot-cakes an' they didn't give him none. He kicked an' pawed the ground so furious that the wind it made blowed over the cook-shanty. Then he made straight fer it an' et up all the cakes, an' then he got so greedy he swallered the stove an' died o' 'cute indigestion. They butchered him right thar an' salvaged the stove an' shipped the meat away in sixty box-cars; an' folks 've complained o' tough beefsteak ever since.

An' now I'm done yarnin'. Them wuz great ol' days. — Guess I'll go on up the Mackenzie an' git m'self a job a-cookin'.